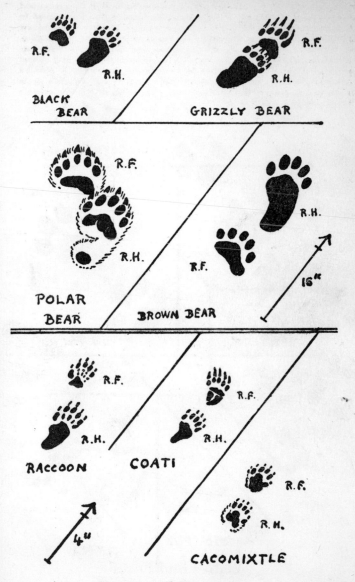

Bears and Raccoons

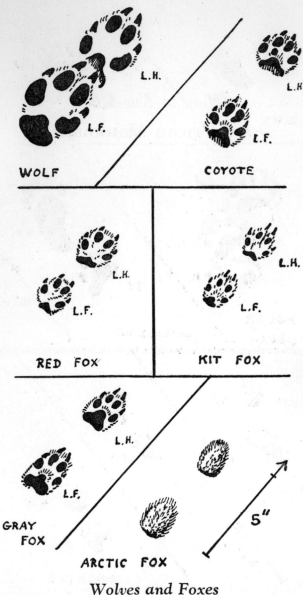

WOLF

COYOTE

L.H.

L.F.

L.K

L.F.

RED FOX

KIT FOX

L.K.

L.F.

L.H.

L.F.

GRAY FOX

ARCTIC FOX

L.H.

L.F.

5"

Wolves and Foxes

Illustrations of imprints continued on page 165.

How to Know the
American Mammals

HOW TO KNOW THE
American Mammals

by

Ivan T. Sanderson

WITH FULL LINE DRAWINGS BY THE AUTHOR
AND FULL-COLOR PLATES BY
LOUIS AGASSIZ FUERTES

Little, Brown and Company · Boston

1951

ACKNOWLEDGMENTS

The author wishes to express his sincerest thanks to Mr. T. Donald Carter, Assistant Curator of Mammals at the American Museum of Natural History, New York, for having read the text of this work, and for having checked all data against the most recent findings of scientific research in this field.

My thanks are due also to Dr. Clarence Cottam, Assistant Director of the U.S. Fish and Wildlife Service of the Department of the Interior, for having read the manuscript from the point of view of one entrusted with the preservation of our wild fauna.

599
S

*Published simultaneously
in Canada by McClelland and Stewart Limited*

PRINTED IN THE UNITED STATES OF AMERICA

This book is dedicated

to

HAZEL GAY

Librarian of the American Museum of Natural History, without whose unique knowledge of zoological literature and unstinted help so many books would never be written.

CONTENTS

I. ABOUT MAMMALS

All *Mammals* are animals—for they are manifestly neither vegetable nor minerals—but all *Animals* are not mammals. How then may we define mammals? A scientist would define mammals as those back-boned animals with warm blood, that bear live young which they suckle with milk developed in their own bodies, and have hairs. However, to answer this question it is better to state what they are not and simply to say that they are those animals with backbones made up of little separate bones, or vertebrae, which are neither birds, reptiles, amphibians, nor fishes. This is easy enough to say but it is not a fact that is easy to demonstrate, even with the animal before you. The status of whales, bats, men, and the manatee have always puzzled people, so let us give some more positive definitions. Mammals alone among animals suckle their young with milk produced in the mother's body, although some lay eggs—the Platypus and the Echidna. Mammals have warm blood, though some of them look like fish—the Whales. Mammals alone grow real hair, although some birds have whiskers and an African frog has a fringe of hair-like skin along its flanks. Even whales have hairs; the porpoise has a moustache composed of just two. Mammals are the most varied group of the backboned animals and they range in size from the Pygmy Shrew of Europe, weighing less than a dime, to the greatest creature that has, as far as we know, ever lived on this planet, the Blue Whale which may weigh up to 125 tons or the equivalent of a hundred million Pygmy Shrews.

Mammals are divided unequally among eighteen major groups, called *orders*. The animals grouped in each of these are actually related by evolutionary links and not just by similarity of form. These orders are further divided into what are called *families*, all the members of which are still more closely related, and these in turn contain a varying number of *genera* of which the individual groups or members—called *species*—are even more like each other. There are some 10,000 known species of mammals living in the world today.

In North America we have examples of 10 of the 18 major groups or *orders* but three of these are represented by only one species—namely the order *Edentata* by the Armadillo, the *Marsupialia* by the Opossum, and the order *Sirenia* by the Manatee. Of the remaining seven orders, the Mammals that Gnaw, or the *Rodentia,* with nine indigenous and two introduced families, are by far the most important, being represented by no less than 40 genera and over 300 species. Next come the Flesh-Eaters, or *Carnivora,* with 25 genera and 143 species; then the Shrews and Moles, or *Insectivora,* with 11 genera and 53 species; the Whales and Dolphins, or *Cetacea,* with 26 genera but only 41 species; the Bats, or *Chiroptera,* with 13 genera and 37 species; the Even-toed Hoofed Ones, or *Artiodactyla,* with 10 genera and 35 species; and, last, the Seals, or *Pinnipedia,* with 9 genera and 13 species. Thus we have about 650 species of mammals in North America and its surrounding seas. North America is herein to be understood as covering the territory of the United States, Canada and its Arctic islands, and Greenland and Alaska.

Whether you live in the country or in a town, are interested in wildlife or not, and regardless of whether you have ever been to a zoo, you will find that you already know a large number of mammals. Who does not know a bat, cat, dog, fox, bear, seal, squirrel, rat, mouse, rabbit, pig, deer, cow, sheep, goat, or whale when he sees one? There are also a great number of people who have at least heard of moles, cougars, bobcats, raccoons, weasels, minks, otters, skunks, badgers, sea lions, walruses, groundhogs, prairie-dogs, flying squirrels, gophers, muskrats, woodrats, porcupines, moose, elk, reindeer, bison, armadillos, porpoises, and dolphins. And when you have named these you will find there are not many more kinds of North American mammals left to be enumerated. In fact, there is nothing to be depressed about until you try to differentiate between one kind of bat, shrew, fox, weasel, rat, marmot, mouse, rabbit, deer, whale, or dolphin, and another. Even then, except with rats and mice, it is usually rather simple, as we shall try to show; all of which conveniently answers the question, what is a mammal?

WHERE ARE THE MAMMALS?

This is an even more difficult question to answer although it could quite easily and truthfully be avoided simply by answering, "everywhere." Mammals live on the arctic ice and sometimes under it; they live in all seas and oceans, in waterless deserts, in jungles, woods, and scrub, on grassy steppes and prairies, on farms, in swamps, in lakes and rivers, in trees, in holes in the ground, in caves, in the air, and even in towns. They go wherever we go, simply and automatically because we ourselves are mammals. Only on the wastes of the antarctic ice cap, on mountains above the perpetual snowline, and in the depths of the oceans are they not, as far as we know, found.

Although mammals occur everywhere, not all kinds do so, as is perhaps obvious. Nobody would look for a deer in a treetop or a whale in a backyard. Moreover, the shape and size of mammals give us certain intuitive clues as to where they may live. Little, quick ones with hand-like paws and fluffy tails to balance their bodies live in trees; long ones with short limbs and tapering tails live in or by water; long-legged ones with hooves run on the ground and in open places; small, compact ones with sharp claws dig; those with long back legs jump over the ground. Then there are special animals that dig, like the armadillos, that are clothed in armor-plate for protection, and certain compressed, furry ones like the porcupines, raccoons, and bears which wander about and are equally at home in a variety of places.

The land surface of the earth can be divided into a number of great "Animal Countries," the boundaries of which are natural and not political. Our North American continent contains four such countries—the Arctic Tundra, the Boreal Forests of Canada, the "West," and the Woodlands of the East. Each of these can be subdivided into a number of "Natural Provinces." Our Arctic contains Greenland, Labrador, the Canadian Arctic Islands, a north central Territory, and Alaska. The Boreal Forest country is the most homogenous, but embraces distinct eastern, central, and western provinces. The "West" is the most varied, being made up of a string of narrow Provinces running from north to south on the Pacific coast, the mountain areas of the Rockies and other ranges, the central Prairies, and the scrub zones and deserts of the Southwest. The eastern Woodlands range from what is technically known as the Great Lakes Area in the north, to the Louisiana swamplands and the sub-tropics of Florida in the south. Each of these "Animal Countries" and each of their included "Natural Provinces" is inhabited by a distinctive group of mammals. Within them also are smaller units, and these again are split up by natural boundaries and divisions which limit the range of certain species and groups of species.

However, some mammals normally range far, while others migrate annually, and there is also a slow spread of species always going on in accordance with certain long-term changes of climate. Thus, the Armadillo has now crossed the Mississippi and reached Alabama, and the Coyote has arrived in Ohio. Most are, however, confined to limited natural provinces within which they tend to fill every available niche. Thus, even among the flesh-eating weasels, there is a species in the trees (the Marten), on the damp ground and in the trees (the Fisher), on dry ground (the True Weasels), on the borders of streams (the Mink), and in the water (the Otter). Mammals, in fact, are where you find them, but they are there, you will always find, for very special and definite reasons. One of these is that "Nature abhors a vacuum" and always manages to fill it.

Although mammals are so numerous and widespread, they are, comparatively speaking, very seldom seen. Unlike reptiles, many of which move about in the sunlight, or birds, which are so obvious all around us every day, most mammals move about by night. However, they often leave evidence of their passing in the form of tracks in soft earth, mud, or on snow. Each mammal leaves different imprints and the arrangement of these imprints forming the track varies according to the speed and method of travel—whether a walk, a trot, a run, a canter, a gallop, etc. Learn to identify tracks and you soon find and learn to know the mammals.

II. ANCIENT MAMMALS

1. BATS

The Bats, or *Chiroptera* (*cheiron*, a hand, and *pteron*, a wing), are usually placed next to the lemurs, monkeys, apes, and ourselves, at the top of the scheme of life. They are specialized mammals with relatively large brains, but they display certain primitive characters showing that they branched off the main stem of the mammalian family tree very long ago.

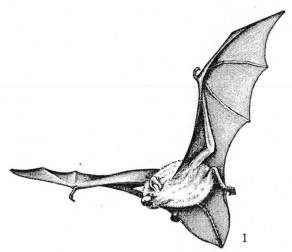

1

Bat in Flight

Bats are found throughout the world from the Arctic Circle almost to the Antarctic. They form the second largest order of mammalian species, some of which may be found sleeping together in millions in one cave, while a single hollow tree in Africa has yielded over a thousand individuals. All bats have wings formed by delicate skin membranes stretched between the four greatly elongated fingers of their hands and thence to the sides of their bodies and to their legs. Most bats also have a membrane stretching between the hind legs, which may extend to the tip of the tail, only partly enclose the tail, stretch below it, or, if the species is tailless, hardly exist at all. The thumb is small and remains free. Almost all bats rest and sleep hanging upside down suspended by either one or both hind feet. A few, however, like some of the Mastiff Bats and the true Vampire Bats, can fold their wings tightly and run about on all fours.

Bats are divided into two groups known as the *Mega-* (large) and *Micro-* (small) *chiroptera*, but some of the "Large" ones are small and some of the "Small" ones are quite large. The distinction between the two groups is based on more than mere size. "Large" bats are found only in the Old World and include the largest, an East Indian Flying Fox, with a body the size of a crow, that is very good to eat, and which has a wingspan of over five feet. The smallest lives in and flies above the trees of the African forests and has a body no bigger than the smallest hummingbird's. All our American bats are "Small" bats and without exception are comparatively small in size.

Most bats feed on insects which they catch and eat while on the wing, but the "Large" bats and a few "Small" bats eat fruit, while two species eat fish which they catch by flying over still water and dipping into its surface with their muzzles, and two live exclusively on the blood of other animals—the only mammals that are parasites.

Of all the interesting things about bats, perhaps the most intriguing is their sonar. Most of the "Small" bats have very small eyes, sometimes mere pinpoints, hidden under the fur on their faces. Nevertheless they find their way unerringly in total darkness through tangled vegetation and tiny tunnels in caves. This they do by emitting through their nostrils periodic bursts of supersonic sound —of frequencies up to 30,000 per second and as short as two hundredths of a second each—that are relatively more noisy than a four-engined bomber in flight. Sometimes complex arrangements of skin flaps around the nostrils aid in beaming these waves which, striking obstacles ahead, are reflected back to the flying bat and picked up by its sensitive ears, aided by complicated structures known as *tragi* and *antitragi* or "false-ears" and possibly by other devices. These are tuned to the reflected air wavelets, and through them the bat detects the obstacles ahead and can then instantly pull in a wing or otherwise alter its course.

In the fall some species of bats, or sometimes only the females, migrate from the colder regions of the north for hundreds of miles towards the tropics. Those which do not do so, hibernate sometimes for up to six months. During hibernation the body temperature of mammals usually drops to just above the freezing point, but that of some bats has been found actually to fall below so that hoarfrost forms on their fur. Their breathing rate may drop from as high as 150 respirations to as low as six, and their pulse rate from 250 to 170 per minute, while to compensate for the reduced amount of oxygen, carried in the red corpuscles of their blood, the number of white corpuscles increases enormously.

Most bats fly at night or in the morning and evening. However, there are South American bats that pursue insects like swallows, over rivers by day, and several species climb up into the sky long before sundown to catch day-flying insects and then, following these, slowly descend, arriving back on the ground after dark. Bats have a strong but erratic flight because they actually *claw* their way through the air rather than *gliding* or *swimming* through it like birds. However, the "Large" Fruit-bats, which have shoulder joints more like other mammals may have a very steady flight. As in birds, narrow, sharply tapering wings mean speed; short wide wings a more butterfly-like, fluttering flight.

Bats are not attracted by women's hair nor do they become entangled in it if placed therein. Although bats carry various parasites, these are mostly small wingless flies called Streblids which, like the fleas and ticks found on these animals, will not infest men. Bats should never be killed as they are not only harmless but by eating enormous quantities of insect pests contribute materially to our comfort and economy.

A. LEAF-NOSED BATS

These are known technically by the tongue-twister *Phyllostomatidae* which means simply the leaf, *phylla*, nostril, *stomata*, ones. They form a large family with headquarters in South America, and some of them have taken to eating fruit like the Old World *Megachiroptera*, and are of considerable size with a wing span of almost three feet. They are distinguished by bearing a dagger- or petal-shaped, upright, fleshy structure on their muzzles. The range of only one species reaches our borders.

2

Large-eared Bat

(1) The Large-eared Bat

This species (see Fig. 2) is notable, as its technical name *Macrotis* implies (the one with *macros*, large, *otis*, ears) for the size of its ears. But it is also the only one of our bats which has a "nose-leaf." It is really a Mexican animal, but migrates north to California and adjacent southwestern states in summer. It is a large bat, dull brown in color, but if you blow the fur apart, you will find that it is actually white, the individual hairs being only tipped with brown. The ears are very large and widely expanded and there are tall but thin, prominent, pale-colored false-ears within them. The wings of this bat are rather short but wide, and the membrane between the hind limbs is so narrow that the "knees" are held close together. The tail is composed of five, very long, slender bony sections the last of which extends beyond the membrane. The ears are connected by a narrow up-right band of furred flesh extending across the top of the head.

B. EVENING BATS

The *Vespertilionidae* (from *vespertilio* meaning the "evening ones," a word used by the Romans for all bats) is the largest of all the bat families, being found almost all over the world, but especially in the northern hemisphere. Thirty-one of the thirty-seven bats found in North America are Evening Bats and they are divided among ten distinct types or genera which we shall try to identify below. This is not easy to do, since no less than 18 of the 31 belong to one genus and vary considerably in size and color, while they closely resemble the members of the two following genera.

(1) Little Brown Bats

This may sound like a purely artificial title, but it is widely recognized. To distinguish the eighteen Little Brown Bats (genus *Myotis*), Fig. 3, from each other and from the next two genera is very difficult. There are a few exceptionally colored species, but the majority are of various shades and combinations of brown from pale cream to golden chestnut or darkest sepia, usually lighter below. However, there is both regional and individual color variation within many species. Further, the ears vary in size considerably and the body dimensions and tail length range from three to four inches and one to two inches respectively. The face is "simple," the muzzle naked, pointed, and slightly swollen but unadorned with blisters or other devices. The ears are small and rather pointed. There is no fur on the arms or legs and the medium-long tail is completely enclosed in the interleg membrane, which is further supported, as in almost all bats, by two bony spurs extending backwards from the ankles. The wingspread is about eleven inches. Little Brown Bats are usually the common small bats in any area, sleeping in caves, houses and trees. One distinctive species is called the White-edged Bat, from California. It is light buff above and white below and has a white edge to the wing membranes. A southern form is gray, rather than brown, and another has the back edge of the interleg membrane thickly furred. The various species of Little Brown Bats are found throughout the continent south of the Arctic wastelands in suitable localities.

(2) Big Brown Bats

These bats (genus *Eptesicus*), Fig. 5, are fairly common and often enter houses even in towns and cities and may go so far as to hibernate therein. They are brown in color, lighter below, and have dark, naked, tough ears and membranes. The body averages three and a half and the tail one and a half inches. The face is naked and unadorned but for a few coarse hairs, and the ears are erect but incline forward. The false-ears are small and roundly pointed, the lips fleshy, bearing a slight moustache. The body fur extends somewhat on to both the upper- and undersurfaces of the wing membranes. These bats squeak a lot while in flight, are nocturnal, and prefer open places. They are strong, purposeful fliers, and are found throughout the country.

(3) Pipistrelles

These (genus *Pipistrellus*), Fig. 4, are the smallest of our bats, one being only two inches in body length with a one-inch tail. They are primarily rock bats and rest singly in caves where they may hibernate in great numbers deep in the earth. They are of a rather light brown color, and the interleg membrane reaches to the tail tip and has a light fluff of fur on its front upper half. The face is simple and mousy. The flight of Pipistrelles is more fluttery and agile than that of the Brown Bats. There are two kinds, one in the eastern states and the other in the Southwest; the latter extends north to Montana.

(4) The Silvery Bat

This bat (genus *Lasionycteris*), Fig. 6, although similar in form to the above, is easy to identify because its fur is long and colored like a silver fox, being very dark brown or black, tipped with white. There are several rows of tiny warts, each bearing a few hairs, running across the upper half of the interleg membrane. The body is a little under three inches long and the one-and-a-half-inch tail is completely enclosed in this membrane. The single species is found spottily throughout the continent but nowhere else. It may be found in caves but appears to be a forest species preferring trees.

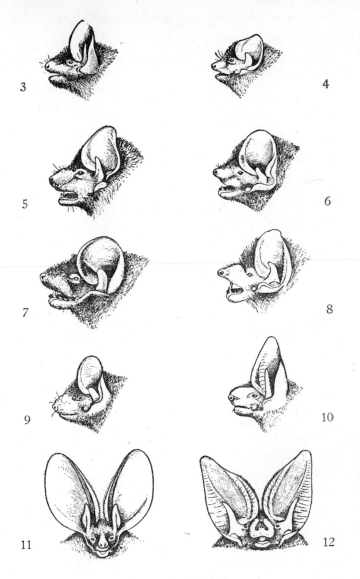

3

4

5

6

7

8

9

10

11

12

EVENING BATS

2

(5) The Red and Hoary Bats

The genus *Nycteris* or "night ones," Fig. 7, contains two long-tailed bats, two and three inches in body length respectively, and both with two-inch tails. The first has long, red fur which thickly covers the top of the interleg membrane, light shoulder patches, black-edged, furry ears, and fur on the underarm up to the wrist. It is found all over the country. The Hoary Bat is larger and has fur the individual hairs of which are black at the base, then pale cream, then chocolate, and finally tipped with white on the upper, and with yellowish on the underside of the body. The membranes of both are almost black. Both are forest bats. Both bear up to four young at a time, which the mother manages to carry when on the wing, even though their combined weight may be more than her own.

(6) Yellow Bats

Compact, long-tailed bats with bun-shaped bodies of a tropical genus (*Dasypterus*), Fig. 8, the larger of which occurs in Texas and is three and a half inches in length. The other, only two and a half inches in body length, is Floridian. They are light brownish-yellow above with dark markings, and reddish-yellow below. The ears are short, broad, and oval, slightly hairy within and furred halfway up their outer sides. The fur is long and silky and extends halfway on to the upper half of the interleg membranes and along the underside of the forearm. They sleep alone in deep caves.

(7) The Leaf-tailed Bat

A species known to science as *Nycticeius humeralis*, Fig. 9, which is found in the southeastern states, the Mississippi Valley, and Texas. It is only two inches long, ashy-gray in color, with a brown neck, and has a very distinct tail arrangement. The tip of the one-and-a-half-inch tail protrudes beyond the heart-shaped interleg membrane which is supported by very small ankle spurs and which has a series of pronounced parallel veins bowing downwards and forming a herringbone pattern. The ears are small, erect and rounded, and the muzzle is naked and rather rough-looking. The membranes are completely naked and almost black.

(8) The Spotted Bat

This bat, Fig. 11, known as *Euderma maculata*, is small-bodied, but has large wings, and very distinctive coloring. The fur is of the darkest brown, but on the underside appears to have been lightly painted over with pale cream. Large, odd-shaped, white spots cover the shoulders and the rump. The membranes are pale buff. This bat has positively enormous ears joined together by a curious, crinkled, upright band of skin crossing the forehead. The false-ear is very tall and almost paddle-shaped. Very few specimens of this bat have ever been caught, and the nature of its resting place is unknown but it appears to be wholly nocturnal and a high flier. It has only been taken in the southwestern deserts.

(9) The Pallid Bat

Antrozous pallidus, Fig. 10, also has large but pointed ears with numerous delicate cross-ridges. The false-ears are tall, thin, and scalpel-shaped. The eyes are rather large and the muzzle is swollen and bears a crease above the nostrils, which point slightly downwards. The wings are short and broad, the tail moderate, and the interleg membrane is triangular and supported by long heel spurs. The pellage is a light brownish-gray with dark stippling and the membranes are also light. The body measures two and a half and the tail one and a half inches. Pallid bats are found only in the Southwest and are cliff dwellers, but hunt their prey both in the air and over the ground, from which they pick it up with their teeth while in flight.

(10) Lump-nosed Bats

There is no mistaking these (*Corynorhinus*) bats, Fig. 12. They are small with moderately long tails and huge pointed ears joined across the head with the usual band, and with tall, narrow, false-ears. The nostrils open like geysers, in a curious, heart-shaped swelling on the top of the muzzle. The interleg membrane is very large and leaf-shaped with long ankle spurs, and its veins bow upwards. The fur color varies widely but there is always a white area around the base of the ears. These bats occur over most of the United States and in British Columbia.

C. MASTIFF BATS

The other bats found in North America belong to a tropical family called *Molossidae* named after a breed of dogs known to the ancient Greeks as Molossus. Their faces are somewhat dog-like. They all have narrow wings for speedy flight, and their mouse-like tails protrude from the middle of the interleg membrane. Many have strange, club-shaped bristles on their muzzles and peculiar, in-folded, forward-projecting ears. Two species are found in North America.

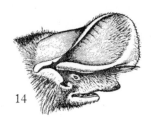

Mastiff Bats

The smaller Free-tailed Bat (*Tadarida*), Fig. 13, occurs from Alabama to California and north to Nevada, Nebraska, and Iowa. It is about three inches long, with a one-inch tail protruding from the small interleg membrane which is almost enclosed by the large ankle spurs. *Tadarida* are dark brown above, lighter below, and the fur is very short and velvety. The body is solid and they are active crawlers. They are gregarious, and while common in caves, readily take up their abodes in houses and show little fear of humans. Their ears are joined together on top of their heads. The larger Bonnet Bat (*Eumops*), Fig. 14, is four and a half inches long with a two-inch tail; it is found in Texas and the extreme Southwest. Its fantastic ears are joined all along over the head and project beyond the nose. The interleg membrane is small and wrinkled and the feet, like those of *Tadarida*, bear a fuzz of long, stiff, recurved hairs on their upper sides and are used to brush the fur. *Eumops* is rare and found only in a few scattered localities.

2. INSECT-EATERS

Zoologists often apologize for using this order of mammals, which they call the *Insectivora*, as a sort of wastebasket to contain an assortment of small creatures having little in common except a number of obviously ancient anatomical features. If extinct forms known from fossil teeth and bones be taken into consideration, however, it will be found that they are basically related. They come near the bottom of the mammal family tree, yet they seem to be an offshoot of our own ancestors, for the Tree-Shrews still living in Malaya today form a direct link between them and the Primate Mammals to which group we belong. Only two of the eight families comprising the *Insectivora* are represented in North America—the Moles and the Shrews. The other families are those of the Hedgehogs, Tenrecs, Elephant-Shrews, Golden-Moles, the Otter-Shrew of West Africa and the Solendons of Haiti and Cuba.

A. MOLES

Members of this family, known as the *Talpidae*, from the Latin word *talpa*, are not likely to be mistaken for any other animal. They spend most of their lives underground burrowing for insects, worms, and other small fry. They have pointed muzzles and minute eyes, and bodies shaped not unlike Idaho potatoes. The front paws stick out of the side of the body, are almost circular, face backwards, and bear five tremendous digging claws. The hind legs are very small but work vertically, pushing the body forward as the paddle does a sternwheel riverboat. The tail is sensitive and used as a feeler to warn of nasty things behind, and aid in traveling backwards along tunnels, at which astonishing behavior moles are most adept. The fine, silky fur of moles is devised to facilitate going in reverse, for the hairs grow straight up and can as well be brushed forwards as backwards. Although a five-year-old child can crush a mole between his fingers, these animals are incredibly strong and are said to be able to raise a man by tunneling under his feet. The moles of the eastern states are quite different from those of the Pacific coast, while the Rockies form a moleless belt running down the western states.

(1) Common Moles

The animals we call Common Moles occur from Massa-chusetts to Florida and thence west to Nebraska in the north and Texas in the south. They vary in overall length —i.e. from nose to tip of tail—from five to eight inches and in color from dark gray-brown, with pale cream muzzle, feet and tail, which is short and almost hairless, to coppery-brown with pinkish-orange fleshy parts. They are slightly lighter in color in summer and the under-parts are always a little more clear in tone than the upper. The toes of the hind feet are joined together by webs which led to their misleading Latin name, *Scalopus aqua-ticus*. Quite contrary to being aquatic, they prefer well-drained pastures and open woods where they make bur-rows about ten inches below the surface and send up their

15

Common Mole

well-known "molehills." They also construct a nest lined with grass and leaves, about six inches in diameter, and usually below roots or other protection, in which a single litter of two to five young are produced about April. The young are naked and quite blind, but are able to care for themselves within a month after birth. Common Moles do not hibernate even in the North. They appear to be solitary animals, each occupying its own series of tunnels except at the mating season when they may be found pushing themselves along the surface, presumably in search of a mate. Any damage they do to lawns is quite trivial compared to the good they do by eating countless tons of garden insect pests every year. However, they also consume vast quantities of earthworms which are bene-ficial because they break up the soil. Nevertheless the moles themselves do likewise and often on as great a scale.

(2) Western Moles

Except for a slightly larger average size—six to nine inches—and less tendency to brownish pellage, the Western Moles (Fig. 16) resemble the Common Moles. However, they have eight more teeth, and are really quite different animals; their Latin name is *Scapanus*. They inhabit a narrow belt of lowlands along the Pacific coast from the Canadian border about Puget Sound to Mexico. In habits they are similar to the Common Mole but they throw up slightly larger hills.

(3) The Hairy-tailed Mole

In some localities, but not many, throughout an area extending from New Brunswick, southern Quebec and Ontario, to Ohio in the west, Connecticut in the east, and North Carolina, via the Appalachians, in the south, may be found another mole (Fig. 17) *Parascalops—para*, like, *scalopus*, the common species—easily distinguished by its tail which, as its popular name implies, is hairy as opposed to naked. Moreover, besides being short and thickly clothed in long hairs, the tail is about four times as fat as that of the Common Mole and is shaped like a bowling pin. The hind toes are not joined by webs. This species, besides inhabiting open pastures on the lowlands, is found in dense forests where the soil is loose, and up mountains to at least 3000 feet. It spends more time on the surface than the Common Mole and appears to breed somewhat later. The average size is about six inches and its head is noticeably shorter than that of the Common Mole.

(4) The Star-nosed Mole

This unique animal, *Condylura cristata* (Fig. 18), is our most fabulous-looking mammal because of the twenty-two little, light-pink, fleshy fingers that grow out of its nose in the form of a star. This singular structure is highly sensitive and aids the animal in probing for its food, more especially in the mud of swamps and even at the bottom of ponds and streams. It is altogether less potato-shaped than the species mentioned above, and the spatulate forepaws are used like the flippers of a seal for

16

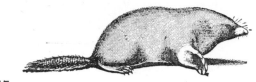

17

18

19

MOLES

swimming. The hind legs are longer, and the tail somewhat compressed, making an effective scull. It inhabits damp, soggy soil near swamps and streams from Labrador, Quebec and Ontario west to Manitoba and thence south to Illinois, Indiana, and Ohio, and via the northeastern United States to Virginia and North Carolina. Burrows near water sometimes have an underwater entrance and are often filled with water, but the nest is placed in an elevated mound above flood level. In winter it burrows in the snow and even wanders about on its surface. It is almost black in color, the eye is noticeable but still small. The tail is almost half as long as the body and in winter swells up enormously, being a fat-storage organ. The food consists not only of insects and worms, but also of a variety of aquatic creatures and occasionally small fish.

(5) The Shrew-Mole

On the lowlands of the Pacific coast from British Columbia to California is found the *Neurotrichus* (Fig. 19), which links the moles to the shrews. Its body is mole-like but even less potato-shaped than that of the Star-nosed Mole, while its head is longer, more pointed, and has a naked muzzle. The forepaws are much longer than they are wide, and bear tremendous claws; the thick tail is about half as long as the head and body, but is narrow at the base and bears a few hairs and rings of tiny scales. In color it is very dark gray to black above and somewhat lighter below. Full grown animals reach an overall length of four and a half inches, of which one and a half inches is tail.

HOW TO KNOW THE MOLES

(1) In the East and Middle West:
    (a) With fleshy star on nose........Star-nosed Mole
    (b) Ordinary, with naked tail........Common Mole
    (c) Ordinary, with hairy tail......Hairy-tailed Mole

(2) On the Pacific slopes:
    (a) Ordinary, with naked tail.........Western Mole
    (b) Long, slender, and small............Shrew-Mole

B. SHREWS

The second family of Insectivores found in North America is known as the *Soricidae* from the Roman name *sorex* for the shrew. The smallest mammal in the world is one of the Pygmy Shrews which weighs less than a dime. Shrews abound throughout the temperate and tropical regions of Africa, Eurasia, North and Central America, yet they are seldom seen and their very existence is unknown to the majority. They are exceedingly delicate little creatures with very fine, soft fur, long tapering snouts, pinhead-size eyes, and complexly infolded ears that are usually almost buried in the fur. They live in close association with wild mice, which they resemble only very superficially, and from which they may be readily distinguished by their numerous, small, sharply-pointed, orange-colored teeth. They exude a strong musky odor from glands on their flanks, and inhabit low, tangled vegetation and the underlying leaf-mold wherever it affords them protection, where there are rodent runways or tunnels, and where there is an ample supply of insect and other small animal food. In temperate regions shrews bear from one to four litters of up to nine young per year between early spring and late summer. They do not appear to breed in their first year, and it seems that they die off at the end of their second breeding season since large numbers are often found dead in the fall. Certain species of shrews, in West Africa for instance, are subject at irregular intervals to sudden enormous increases in numbers and at these times all the individual members of the species affected may also grow into veritable giants. Though the most fragile of all mammals, shrews are unbelievably voracious and irascible and will often attack animals many times their own size, devour more than their own weight in an hour, and digest an equivalent bulk in the same brief period. They are also given to cannibalism.

(1) *Water Shrews*

These, our largest shrews (Fig. 20), which have long tails, and may exceed seven inches in length, can be recognized by their color. This is sharply divided into dark upper- and light undersides, the latter usually silvery white. They also have fringes of stiff bristles along the outer edges of the toes of their hind feet to aid them in swimming. Although they are found all across Canada from Labrador to Alaska and from the northern United States via the uplands down to California in the west and Pennsylvania in the east, and despite their abundance in many areas, very little is known about these animals. They live by streams and marshes and spend most of their time in the water diving for food. Their

Water Shrew

20

thick, soft fur entraps a layer of air bubbles which makes them very buoyant so that they have to swim with all their might to stay below the surface. What is more astonishing is that they can even run for considerable distances *over* the water, being supported by its surface tension and aided by their fringed feet and their speed. Their tracks are very distinctive.

(2) The Gray Shrew

In the drier parts of a somewhat limited area extending from Texas to southern California may occasionally be found the rarest of American shrews (Fig. 21), a small, three-and-a-half-inch, short-tailed, gray animal with white underparts. It is slender in build and may be readily identified by its large, prominent, naked ears. Virtually nothing is known about its habits. Zoologists call it *Notiosorex crawfordi*. It has a prominent white area on its mid-back.

(3) Common Shrews

No less than three dozen species of Common Shrews (*Sorex*) (Fig. 22), all very much alike, are recognized by zoologists as inhabiting North America, spread over the whole country from above the Arctic Circle to Mexico. The interested amateur can spot this genus if upon finding a shrew he will ask himself three questions: (a) is it less than three and a half inches in total length, (b) is the tail less than a quarter the length of the head and body, (c) is its underside white? If the answer to all these questions is "no," then it is a Common Shrew. In color the species vary from chestnut brown to slate gray above; the underside is always slightly lighter. The tail is clothed in hair and is often lighter below. The size ranges from three and a half to six inches, of which more than a third is tail. The small ears are almost completely hidden in the fur.

These shrews inhabit damp locations where the ground cover is thick, both in forested and open areas. They are active by day and night but spend most of their time under cover. They range from high above the timberline on mountains and from the open arctic tundras to the depths of the forests and even to coastal mudflats and salt marshes where their runways may be periodically flooded by the tides. They do not hibernate but are active even in sub-zero cold, burrowing in and often running about on the surface of the snow. In some species the tail swells up in winter with a store of fat.

(4) The Pygmy Shrew

It is by no means easy for any but a specialist to distinguish the Pygmy Shrews—*Microsorex* (Fig. 23)—from the Common Shrews. The tail of both species is more than a third the length of the head and body, but the Pygmy Shrews are considerably smaller—three to four, as opposed to three and a half to six, inches in length. In color they are brown above, and gray, washed with pale buff, below. They range from Nova Scotia to Alaska and south to a line drawn from Washington to Wisconsin, thence around the southern edge of the Great Lakes and the St. Lawrence River to Maine. An isolated race occurs

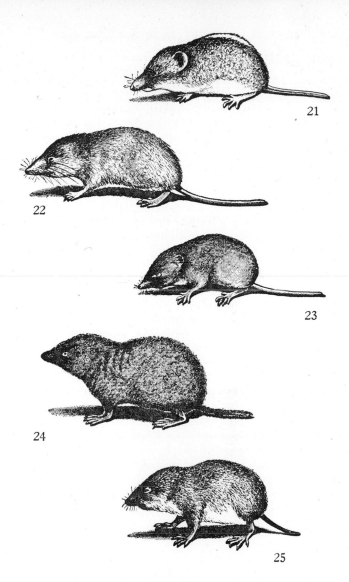

SHREWS

in the Appalachians from Maryland to Georgia. This mammal is so tiny that small specimens can force their way into the holes left by large earthworms. The young are so small that two can be placed on the butt of a pencil.

(5) Greater Short-tailed Shrews

These Short-tailed Shrews, Fig. 24, are to be distinguished from the two foregoing types by their tails which are less than a quarter the length of the head and body. Also, as will be seen from Figs. 21 to 25, their bodies are relatively more bulky than those of the Common and Pygmy Shrews. The Greater Short-tailed species (*Blarina*) are denizens of damp places in woods, pastures, and even open prairies and are found from Quebec to Manitoba and thence south to Oklahoma in the west and Florida in the east. Their silky fur is colored dark gray above, slightly lighter on the undersides. The eyes are minute and the ears are buried in the fur. Having powerful forelegs these shrews often dig their own burrows. The nest is large, and during the breeding season the adult animals give off a particularly strong musky stench. (One of the smaller species is figured on p. 31.)

(6) Lesser Short-tailed Shrews

Also known, misleadingly, as "Little Shrews" or *Cryptotis*—i.e. those with *kryptos,* hidden, *otis,* ears—these shrews (Fig. 25) resemble the *Blarina* in every external respect but size. The largest *Cryptotis,* measuring three and a half inches in total length, is smaller than the smallest *Blarina,* but the only reliable way to distinguish a Lesser from a Greater Short-tailed Shrew is to get a lens and count the teeth; the former has 30, the latter 32. Three species of *Cryptotis* cover the eastern United States as far north as New York and west to Nebraska, but the headquarters of the genus is in Central America. This species prefers meadows and marshes to woods and forests, and appears to be less pugnacious than other shrews: at least they are able to live together in small parties. Amazingly, these little mammals have several times been found living contentedly and even raising their young quite unmolested in wild bees' nests.

RED BAT

LITTLE BROWN BAT

LYNX

BOBCAT

3. TOOTHLESS ONES

The order of mammals to which the Armadillos belong is most misleadingly called the *Edentates,* or *e,* without, *dentates,* teeth. It includes also the Anteaters and Sloths, and is essentially a tropical American group. Among these, the anteaters alone are entirely toothless. The sloths have a few peg-like teeth but the armadillos possess numerous teeth; one species in fact has almost a hundred, which is more than twice the normal mammalian allotment. The Edentates are very ancient mammals and the group is believed to have been evolved in the southern half of the New World, whence certain forms like the Giant Ground Sloths once spread north into what is now the United States. Today only one species is found within our borders.

A. THE ARMADILLO

At the beginning of this century this peculiar little animal was to be found only in the southern parts of Texas, but it has now spread northward and eastward, has crossed the Mississippi—though how has not been satisfactorily explained—and reached Alabama and has been introduced into Florida. It is known to science as *Dasypus novemcinctus,* meaning "nine-girdled (*novem,* nine, *cinctus,* girdle) hairy-footed (*dasypus*) one." It grows to a length of almost three feet of which almost half is composed of a long, tapering tail. It is a low-slung beast with short sturdy legs, and all four feet are armed with exceedingly stout digging claws. The ears are large and shaped somewhat like those of a donkey; the head is long and slender with a pig-like muzzle and snout. The whole body is enclosed in a dome-like, tortoise-shaped shell composed of numbers of tiny, checker-like bones formed in the skin and fused solidly together. This shell hangs down almost to the ground on each side of the body like a mantle. There is a separate shield covering the top of the head, and the tail is enclosed in a series of articulated, solid rings diminishing in size. The rest of the head, neck and the undersides are covered in soft skin bearing some hairs. The main body shield is divided into three portions; solid domes covering the shoulders and rump, and a wide central body band composed of nine separate hinged belts. The color is dirty yellowish-brown. Armadillos rest in holes which they excavate among rocks or roots and preferably in places covered with dense, tangled vegetation. They are about by day but more actively at night, and make regular paths radiating in all directions from their holes; and along these they bumble with a determined air and at a steady jog-trot. Their food is all manner of small fry, but principally insects and especially ants of which they consume enormous numbers along with much earth so that their droppings often form little clay marbles. When hunting off their paths they advance jerkily as they probe under the leaves, and although

26

The Armadillo

possessing acute hearing, their other senses are so dim and their powers of concentration so specialized for the pursuit of small things on the ground that they may then be closely approached. However, once they take fright they rush off through the thickest growth at a really unexpected speed. If cornered they put their heads between their legs and snap their whole body together, forming a ball from which only the tail protrudes like a handle. Careful study has disclosed the amazing fact that these armadillos almost invariably give birth to four young at a time, all of them of the same sex, being two pairs of identical twins. Both pairs, what is more, are derived from a single fertilized ovum. Armadillos are prodigious diggers, throwing out earth with their hind feet in a continuous jet. They can disappear into the ground almost more quickly than one can alight from a horse. Related species once occurred as far north as New York.

4. POUCHED MAMMALS

The Marsupials (*marsupium*, a pouch) of today are apparently the direct and almost unchanged descendants of one of the two original branches into which the most ancient mammalian stock was divided. Certain Insect-eaters coexisted with the first marsupials some hundred million years ago, but their present-day descendants have changed much more radically than those marsupials which still survive. Marsupials once existed all over the world, but for some reason still not understood they died out almost everywhere except in Australasia and South America, both island continents until comparatively recent times when a land bridge grew up between the latter and North America. Numerous insect, flesh, and plant-eating marsupials have survived in Australia and its associated islands, where non-marsupial animals—now represented only by bats, the Dingo Dog, and a few small rodents—were not able to compete with them. In South America the arrival of non-marsupials over the land bridge brought about the extinction of all but two families—the Opossums and the Opossum-Rats. The American Opossums (*Didelphidae*), as opposed to the Australian Opossums or Phalangers (*Phalangeridae*), are the oldest of all marsupials which have not only survived practically unchanged for a hundred million years but which are still today not only spreading but successfully carving a niche for themselves in our modern industrial world. Pouches are not developed in all species of marsupials but when present they are situated on the lower belly of the females, and many contain up to more than a dozen teats to which the minute, foetus-like young attach themselves for an extended period before being weaned. In some species the pouch-opening points backwards so that the young have a rear view like that provided by a railroad observation car.

A. OPOSSUMS

Only two very closely allied species are found in North America. These are the Virginian and Texan Opossums (*Didelphis*, or those with *di*, two, *delphis*, reproductive tracts). The latter is confined to the Rio Grande Valley and occurs in two color varieties, one exactly like the Virginian Opossum, the other being almost wholly black. The Virginian Opossum ranges from Florida to upper New York and westward from Texas to the Great Lakes. However, it is steadily extending its range northeast and northwestward. The Opossum is about the size of a large cat but has a long, pointed face like that of a fox, and an array of dog-like teeth. The ears are large, naked, and rat-like. The body is clothed in a dense, cream-white, woolly undercoat through which grows an overcoat of long, black and silver hairs giving a generally grizzled appearance. The face is white, the ears black and white, the lower limbs black, and the tail, which is rat-like and fully prehensile

27

The Opossum

like that of certain South American monkeys, is furred at the base, then naked and black, and finally naked and pinkish-white. The bulging black eyes give a wide vision, and the forepaws with five well-developed, squirrel-like fingers are extremely dexterous. The feet have four clawed toes and a widely opposed "thumb" with a nail. Their digestion is like that of an acid vat and they eat almost everything, flesh, insects, carrion, and vegetable matter. They make nests in hollow trees, logs, among rocks or even in buildings, and produce up to 18 partially developed young after a gestation period of only 12 days. As there are only 13 nipples in the pouch, the excess die immediately, but only about half a dozen normally reach maturity in any case. They do not "play" possum, but rather, it has been learned, suffer automatic trance or coma from shock, making them appear dead.

III. FLESH-EATING MAMMALS

In the order of mammals known to zoologists as the *Carnivora*, from the Latin *carnis*, meaning flesh, and *vorare*, to eat, are brought together a wide variety of creatures of many different sizes, shapes and habits. They are not all by any means exclusively flesh-eaters, and some are pure vegetarians—*e.g.* the Giant Panda. Further, as we have already seen, there are many flesh-eaters that are not members of this order, like the shrews. However, all the members of the *Carnivora* are related through distant ancestry, all having stemmed from creatures known from fossil skeletons, and called Creodonts. Today some carnivores inhabit every part of the land surface of the earth except Antarctica, New Zealand, and certain oceanic islands. Even Australia has the wild Dingo Dog, and every place inhabited by man has domestic dogs and cats. There are seven *families* of *Carnivora* and no fewer than five of these are represented in North America—the Cats, Dogs, Bears, Raccoons, and Weasels. Only the Hyenas of Africa and the Civets of Africa and the Orient are absent. The Americas are the headquarters of the Raccoon family, only two kinds—the Lesser Panda and the Giant Panda of Asia—being found elsewhere.

1. CATS

The cats, although indigenous to every part of Eurasia, Africa, and the Americas, although varying greatly in size and appearance, and although variously divided up by different experts into a long list of genera, are all of remarkably similar structure. Anatomically there is no justification for separating Lions, Leopards, or Jaguarondis from Domestic Cats. The Latin name for the cat was *Felis*, hence all cats are known as the *Felidae*. Despite endless debate, it appears that Domestic Cats are descended from a species called *Felis lybica* which was apparently first tamed by the ancient Egyptians as a retriever of waterfowl, and later to protect granaries from mice. The Wild Cat of Europe, Pallas' Cat of central Asia, and the Tiger Cat of southeastern Asia are quite different animals, but each is believed by one group of "experts" to have contributed some blood to the present-day domestic cat population.

A. GREAT CATS

This title is artificial but is popularly known and serves a useful purpose by breaking up the list of North American cats, of which there are six distinct species.

(1) The Puma

Otherwise known as the Cougar or Mountain Lion, this animal once occurred all over the continent as far north as British Columbia, Alberta, the Great Lakes and Maine, and once had the widest distribution of any known mammal, since it also occurs all over Central and South America from desolate mountain tops to the depths of the equatorial forests. In North America it is now restricted to the western states and small areas in southern Florida

28

The Puma

and New Brunswick. The males are larger than the females and can measure eight feet from nose to tail tip, and weigh up to 230 lbs. They are of a uniform yellowish-to reddish-brown, slightly lighter below with a dark brown tail tip, and ears almost black outside and white inside. The head is rather small for the body and the tail a little over a quarter the total length. Pumas are timid in face of man unless cornered and molested, and are past-masters at keeping out of sight. However, they sometimes proclaim their presence by a variety of ghastly yells and screams, and leave distinctive tracks everywhere, for they are great travelers. They maintain a home den among rocks or dense brush and produce up to five but

normally two young at any time of the year according to
local conditions. The young are a dull tawny color covered with diffuse black spots. There are a few fully authenticated records of Pumas attacking children, but I
do not know of any properly documented case of an un-
provoked attack upon an adult. Pumas prefer wild game
ranging in size from Wapiti to mice, and even such unlikely fare as grasshoppers and scorpions, but they may
take an occasional domestic animal and occasionally become regular stock killers, when they have to be hunted
down and killed. However, their habits in no way warrant the ruthless persecution to which they are subjected
by hunters and so-called sportsmen.

29

The Jaguar

(2) The Jaguar

Our other great cat is much rarer and inhabits only
parts of Texas, New Mexico, and Arizona but has sometimes wandered as far north as central California and
Colorado. Although the variety of Jaguar found in this
country is considerably shorter than the Puma, it is a
much bulkier animal, squat, broad, and rather short-
tailed. It prefers dense vegetation but is also a great traveler. Reports of attacks upon men by this cat are extremely rare, but when encountered it is by no means timid
like the Puma. The coat is a beautiful golden-yellow with
rings or rosettes of black spots. The underside is white
with intense black spots. The spots form rings towards
the tip of the tail. Up to four cubs are born in the spring.

B. SMALL CATS

These are *small* only by comparison with the preceding species, but both considerably exceed the Domestic Cat in bulk.

(1) The Ocelot

There are a number of closely related cats in tropical America that grow to a length of from four to five feet and which are beautifully marked with complex patterns of black spots, rosettes, bars, and wavy longitudinal stripes and blotches on a lighter background which varies from bright yellow like the Jaguar to dull olive-fawn. The chin, throat, and undersides are invariably lighter and sometimes pure white with small black spots. In form they are like diminutive leopards, but the tail is comparatively short and bears black rings and tip. One species or form, known as *Felis pardalis*—i.e., the *Pardus-* or

30

The Ocelot

Leopard-like, *Felis,* cat—is a Mexican animal but ranges into southwestern Texas. The background color is gray-buff. The males grow to over three feet in length with a fifteen-inch tail and may weigh up to forty pounds. The females are slightly smaller. The Ocelot is fairly common in parts of the Rio Grande valley but, being strictly nocturnal, is seldom seen. It inhabits the densest vegetation and is as fully arboreal as possible, though like other cats it is a great traveler. It feeds on any animals it can catch from lizards to deer. Only two cubs are born at a time.

(2) The Jaguarondi

In the dense mesquite scrub of south Texas there also occur in considerable numbers certain plain-colored cats with small heads, bodies about the size of a domestic cat, short limbs, and very long tails. They are sometimes gray and sometimes rust-colored, which represents two color phases of a species known to science most muddlingly (see p. 53) as *Felis cacomitli,* and popularly as the Jaguarondi, which name is just as misleading for they have nothing to do with the Jaguar. This animal is also one of a large group of slender, low-slung felines that occur all over Central and South America and which present zoologists with almost endless opportunities for wrangling and debate. They vary greatly in size and in shape, from short,

31

The Jaguarondi

compact, upright-limbed, ground-living forms to the attenuated rock- and tree-climbing types. There are two schools of thought about these cats and the author inclines to that which believes that the smaller, short-headed types form a distinct species which should be called Eyras, while the larger, long-headed species are the true Jaguarondis. The Texan species is of the latter type and climbs well. They feed on small mammals and birds, and are ideally suited to movement through dense thorn scrub. They are active both by day and night, and bear young at any time of the year in special lairs. Eyras and Jaguarondis are the least cat-like of the true or typical cats and give more the impression of oversized members of the weasel family when seen in life.

C. LYNXES

These are medium-sized cats with long legs, very short tails, and plumes arising from the tips of their ears. There are two very distinct kinds in America.

(1) The Canadian Lynx

A large cat (which can be as much as four feet in overall length, Fig. 33) with long, dense and fluffy, light, creamy-gray fur sprinkled with pale brown, prominent black ear-tufts, dependent cheek ruffs marked with vertical black stripes, a short tail with a prominent black tip, and very large, wide, padded, furry feet. It inhabits the forests of Canada from Labrador to Alaska, and may still be found in the wilder parts of Maine, New Hampshire, and Vermont. In the West its range extends south to Colorado via the mountains. It is a rather slow-moving forest animal that retreats precipitately both as an individual and as a species before man. Its staple food in Canada is the Varying Hare (see p. 88) which it hunts over the snow aided by its own "snowshoes." When the supply fails, as it does from time to time, the Lynx tries to substitute a fare of smaller fry with attacks upon such unlikely animals as foxes and large deer. Nevertheless, large numbers seem to starve to death. It prefers the densest pine forests and is a capable tree climber. The sexes meet and pair off for a short time in winter, and after a gestation period of about 70 days, up to four cubs are born in a carefully concealed lair. The cubs are striped and spotted, and for two weeks are quite blind, but they themselves are ready to breed just a year later.

(2) Bobcats

South of the general range of the Lynx, another short-tailed, long-legged cat represented by half a dozen distinct forms is encountered. These are known as the Bobcats (Fig. 32) and are altogether different both in appearance and habits. They thrive on a much more varied diet of small animal life and they are somewhat indifferent to man; in some places they have even thrived among his agricultural and also industrial installations. Lynx-like in general appearance, the Bobcats may be distinguished

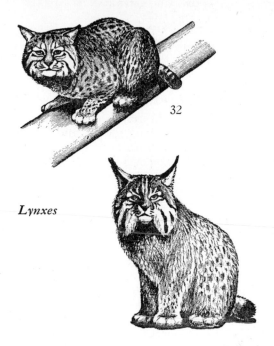

32

Lynxes

33

readily by their smaller feet without furry pads, less prominently plumed or altogether unplumed ears, much less developed but more heavily striped jowl ruffs, broken as opposed to solid black markings that seldom ring the tail, smaller size (maximum three feet six inches overall length), and by their coloration. This varies considerably but is usually reddish- to olive-brown, and is always streaked with black markings. The undersides are lighter, often white, and are often diffusely spotted with black. The backs of the ears are dark to black with a central light spot. Bobcats are wary, retiring, nocturnal creatures preferring thick cover and treeways through which to hunt. There are distinct types on the Pacific coast, on the west slopes of the western mountains, in the deserts of the Southwest, in Florida, and in Nova Scotia, besides the best known variety which is found throughout the eastern states. Two to four furry, spotted young are born in the spring in a den among rocks or thick brush.

2. DOGS

It often comes as a surprise to those who have not been particularly interested in such matters to learn that dogs are related to cats. This relationship is not so close as that between the dogs and bears (see p. 49) but is nonetheless one of common ancestry some 60 million years ago. Dogs are even more widely distributed than cats, for Australia has the Dingo, and Foxes penetrate the wilderness of the Arctic. As a whole, dogs are rather primitive mammals, and are all much alike. Only under the influence of domestication have they become widely diverse.

A. WOLVES

(1) The Wolf

The Wolf (Fig. 34)—*Canis nubilis* from Latin *canis*, a dog, *nubilis*, gloomy, referring to its call—is simply a big, shaggy dog. In color it may vary from brindled gray with cream-gray jowls and underside, to a rusty red, almost jet black, or pure white. Ten "species" of North American wolves have been described, but with the exception of a small species now confined to the lower Mississippi Valley and Texas, they are only regional varieties of one species which is identical to the wolves of Eurasia. Wolves today only remain in any numbers in a few of the wilder areas of the West. The wolf cannot compete with modern man. They bear up to a dozen pups either in burrows which they dig themselves or in a lair in rocks or brush, in April, and travel in family parties several of which may join up in winter. They hunt and kill everything except the large cats, but do not round up large herds of game or, it appears, attack man in packs. In fact, they are rather retiring. Large males may grow to a length of five and one-half feet of which sixteen inches is tail, and weigh up to 150 pounds.

(2) The Coyote

The small, light-bodied wolf (*Canis latrans,* or the "barking" dog, Fig. 35) was until not so long ago a western animal, but it has in recent years spread east to Ohio and has been introduced to almost every eastern state where it has sometimes interbred with feral dogs (see p.

34

Wolves

35

155) . Half a dozen distinct forms are recognized, but with the exception of a small, pale-colored type in the deserts, they are all much alike. Their shaggy fur which is noticeably longer in winter, is grizzled gray with a buffy undercoat and a sprinkling of black hairs. The cheeks, throat, and underside are yellowish-white, and the tail is always black-tipped. Up to seven pups are born in April in regular dens among rocks and brush. In the open wilderness of the West, the Coyote, although always cautious, is wont to proclaim his presence with lonely cries, howls, and yappings, but in many areas where he has encountered man's hostility, he remains silent. In these conditions he manages to thrive and sometimes becomes a pest. Coyotes will readily take to feeding on sheep and other domestic animals and they have sometimes contracted rabies, necessitating all-out destruction. They do not make reliable pets.

B. FOXES

The Foxes (*Vulpes,* from the Latin name for these animals) are simply small, bushy-tailed, burrowing dogs. Certain species, and notably our Red Fox, vary considerably and may occur in two or more distinct color phases.

(1) Red Foxes

A dozen closely related forms of Red Foxes (*Vulpes fulvus,* meaning "the reddish," see Fig. 36) are distributed throughout the continent from the Gulf to the northern limit of trees. They are essentially denizens of broken cover and have adapted well to the changed conditions of modern agriculture. They are traditionally wily animals that hunt mostly by night and are adept at concealment by day. They excavate somewhat capacious burrows in which up to ten pups are born in April, and the parents often literally fall over each other in their solicitude for their offsprings' welfare. The Red Fox serves a most useful service in keeping down the excess rodent-vermin population but its fleetness and fatal habit of adhering to a small area around its home den have aroused the hunting instinct of men from earliest times until today. Red Fox occur in four color forms, sometimes all in the same litter—the normal orange reddish, with white undersides, black stockings, white-tipped tail and black ears; an almost pure black form with white-tipped tail; a semi-melanistic form known to us as the Silver Fox with a varying amount of white-tipped hairs throughout the back and flanks; and the "Cross" variety, is reddish with an almost black band along the back, crossed by another belt over the shoulders from the outer side of one foreleg to the other.

(2) Kit Foxes

The smaller, paler-colored, big-eared, slender-bodied foxes of the open plains and deserts (see Fig. 37), though quite distinct in form, poise, and movements, are customarily regarded as being but specialized types of Red Fox. However, they inhabit a quite different environment, spend more time below ground, have fewer—four to seven—pups at a litter, and fill a special niche in our western prairie and desert fauna.

36

37

38

39

FOXES

(3) Gray Foxes

The *Urocyon* (*oura,* the big-tailed, *kyon,* dog) —see Fig.
38—is altogether different in proportions, gait, and way
of life. It lives all over the United States, except in Maine,
and throughout Central and parts of South America, and
is a denizen of forests—especially the open, lowland pine
barrens—as well as broken cover and scrubland. It is a
great wanderer, and often travels in family parties or
even in small packs. When pursued it is exceedingly swift
and it can climb trees fairly well. Half a dozen pups are
born in a den in a burrow or hollow log in the spring.
In color it is grizzled gray on the head, back and flanks.
The tail is bushy with many black hairs and has a line
of stiff bristles below. The nose and outside of the ears
are black, the cheeks and inside of the ears white. The
undersides are cream white and where they meet the gray
of the uppersides a varying amount of reddish orange in-
tervenes. The pupils of the bright, clear brown eyes are
narrow, vertical ellipses not unlike those of a cat.

(4) Arctic Foxes

Alopex lagopus (the fox with *lagoös,* hare, *pous,* feet)
is an even more distinct creature—see Fig. 39—smaller in
build, with a proportionately much shorter muzzle,
closer, more rounded ears, and smaller teeth. Its habitat
is the arctic tundras north of the pine forests, and in the
long northern winters it ranges out onto the sea-ice where
it feeds upon the remains of the kills of Polar Bears. In
summer its coat is grayish-fawn above and white below;
in winter it turns either pure white all over, which is a
natural camouflage on the open bleakness of snow and ice
floes, or fawn tinged with mauve, when it is known as a
Blue Fox. It is a carrion feeder and cannibalistic when-
ever it encounters a wounded or trapped member of its
own kind. It also has the strange habit of storing large
quantities of small animals and other food in concealed
caches against winter scarcity, the intense cold keeping
the meat fresh for months. As many as a dozen pups are
born in a burrow in early summer, but they have com-
pleted their first moult and are able to care for themselves
by the time the first snows come.

WOLF

COYOTE

WOLVERINE

FISHER

3. BEARS

A much respected zoologist once claimed that there were almost a hundred different species of bears in this country, but the number has now happily been reduced to 30 or to 3, according to how you may choose to define a "species." For those who are interested only in knowing what kind of bear they may meet in a zoo or on a camping trip it should be explained that in North America there are, first, two quite distinct species, the Polar and Black Bears, and secondly, a complex of species comprising the Grizzlies and big Brown Bears, which may appropriately be called the Dish-faced Bears. Bears are simply monstrous, short-tailed dogs, both having evolved from common ancestors, the former only recently.

A. BLACK BEARS

Unfortunately this species—*Euarctos americanus,* the American *Eu,* true, *arctos,* bear; see Fig. 40—is often not black at all but some brown color, when it is customarily called a Cinnamon or Brown Bear. Any two colors may appear as twin cubs from any-colored parents, and an almost pure white race occurs in a limited area in British Columbia. The muzzle is, however, almost always brownish and grizzled sometimes almost to white, and in the black color-form there may be a white spot on the chest. This is a medium-sized bear measuring up to five feet in total length, with powerful but comparatively short claws, and weighing from 200 to 500 pounds when adult. It was once very common throughout the continent, and considerable numbers are still shot annually from Maine to Florida. The Black Bear is completely omnivorous and gorges itself upon almost everything edible, from deer and other large game and small mammals, to wild bees and honey, ants, birds' eggs, berries, fruits, nuts, roots, and even grass and skunk-cabbage. In winter in northern areas they hole up in a retreat and rest for long periods, but they do not truly hibernate because their pulse rate does not drop. Up to three cubs, only about the size of a rat, are born in this retreat, and stay with the mother all summer, fall, and sometimes throughout the following winter.

40

41

42

BEARS

B. DISH-FACED BEARS

Prior to the coming of the white man, a number of partially isolated and distinct populations of bears were scattered throughout a huge belt of territory from Alaska to southern California, and from the islands off the Pacific coast inland to the great plains. Each mountain range and many of the islands appear to have had its distinct race, and there were others, sometimes of gigantic size, that lived on the plains and preyed upon the bison herds. These bears were referred to as Brown Bears or Grizzlies, depending merely upon their color. Many of these have now been totally exterminated, but it is considered that all these often very distinct types, constitute but a complex of closely related species. They range in size from smaller than the Black Bear to the most gigantic carnivore living today, the Kodiak Brown Bear (see Fig. 41) up to ten feet long and standing over four feet at the shoulder, and in color from coal black (the Admiralty Island Bear) to grizzled dark brown, rusty brown, golden or pale cream. The first known Grizzlies (see Fig. 42) inhabited the southern half of the territory and the open plains, but they have now been all but exterminated. However, there are still forms with grizzled pellage and other similar morphological features throughout the Northwest. The typical *Brown* Bears occur only on the Alaskan coast and islands. These animals may be distinguished from Black Bears by the claws on their forefeet which are much larger, sometimes being more than half the length of the sole of the foot. Second, their muzzles seen in profile are straight or downcurved, as opposed to being swollen or upcurved like those of the Black and Polar Bears, and all have pronouncedly humped shoulders. Dish-faced bears inhabit all types of country from bleak mountains and the open salt marshes bordering the Arctic Ocean, to the edges of the hot deserts, open woodlands, and the dense, tangled coniferous forests of the Pacific coast islands. They are completely omnivorous, eating any animal from a bison to an ant, and any kind of fish, as well as fruits, berries, and roots of many kinds. They are dangerous when molested and sometimes even when left alone, and are terrible adversaries.

C. THE POLAR BEAR

The great white bear of the Arctic, *Thalarctos mari-timus*—literally, the maritime, *thal* sea, *arctos* bear—is known to every city school child. Even were it not invariably creamy white in color, it would readily be distinguished by its narrow forequarters, long neck, and small, pointed head with arched muzzle. Males grow to eight feet in length and may weigh as much as three quarters of a ton, though averaging about 1000 lbs. Females are smaller and average only about 750 lbs. The cubs are among the most attractive creatures to be found in nature; with their pure white fluffy fur, black noses, and dark and beady eyes they look like toys. Polar Bears are

43

The Polar Bear

confined to the arctic seaboard whence they range far out on to the polar sea-ice and along its edge. Their food, besides a considerable amount of fish, includes seals and all manner of smaller marine life like crabs and shellfish, and even some seaweeds. On land, moreover, they eat any animals that can be caught and a variety of roots, berries, and other vegetable matter. Twin cubs are born on the ice in midwinter and have to be pushed into the cold waters and taught how to swim by the mother. Although Polar Bears have presumably been hunted by the Eskimo since time immemorial, they remain unafraid of man, and are thus very dangerous, for they will hunt you among broken sea-ice or under cover of darkness. Being expert swimmers they are even more dangerous in the water and have been known to attack small boats.

4. RACCOONS

The fourth family of carnivorous mammals is known as the *Procyonidae*, meaning animals which come before (*pro*) the dogs (*kyon,* Greek for dog). It contains nine diverse animals, seven in the New World—the Raccoon, the Crab-eating Raccoon, the Cacomixtle or Ring-tailed Cat, the Kinkajou, often wrongly called the Honey-Bear, the Coati, the Mountain Coati, and an ambiguous arboreal animal like a Kinkajou but which cannot hang by its tail and which is known as *Bassaricyon* (*kyon,* dog-like, *bassaris, i.e.* Cacomixtle). Three of these occur in North America. The two remaining types are isolated in southeast Asia and are the Panda and the Giant Panda.

A. THE RACCOON

Found from British Columbia, east through Manitoba to Ontario and Maine, and south from this line throughout the continent to Mexico and the keys off Florida where several pale-colored, dwarf races occur. With the exception of the Opossum, the Raccoon is the most versatile of animals, as you will immediately discover if you keep one as a pet. They are easily tamed if caught young, and display the more attractive traits of dogs, cats, and the gentler monkeys, for they can climb almost anything and use their hand-like forepaws with great dexterity. Incidentally, they are inordinately fond of sweet drinks, and if they are not allowed to roll on their backs and drink them out of the bottles, or lap them out of containers, they will dip their paws into the liquid and then avidly lick it off their fingers. If water is available they have a habit of washing their food before eating it, even if they have just caught the item in that same water. Their habits are hard to define because they vary so widely according to locality, habitat, and, apparently, individual taste. They can inhabit almost any type of country except the highest mountaintops and deserts, but they show a decided preference for dampness, be it swamp, lake, stream, river, or the seacoast. They are expert climbers and good swimmers. Their food is almost as varied as that of the bears, and includes almost everything edible, though they show a preference for animal as opposed to vegetable matter, and live animals to carrion, which they often reject with ob-

Raccoons

vious disgust. They move about mostly but not entirely by night, and although they indulge in a lot of deep sleeping in the cold weather in northern climes, they do not truly hibernate, and appear on warm nights to go foraging in the snow. Three to six young are born in mid-spring after a gestation period of about two months, and stay with the mother till fall. At various seasons according to latitude the males indulge in awful squabbles accompanied by wild screams. At other times they mew, whistle, or emit little scratchy barks. A Raccoon is unmistakable with its sturdy body clothed in long, dense, gray fur, its short, full tail ringed in black and white, and its foxy face with black nose, white muzzle and black "mask." Males are said to weigh as much as 45 lbs., but the average is only about 15 lbs.

B. THE CACOMIXTLE

This animal (Fig. 45b) has nocturnal habits and is much more retiring and elusive in character than the Raccoon. It is found only in limited localities west of a line drawn from Oregon to central Louisiana and Alabama. It is known as *Bassaris astutus* (*i.e.*, the astute *bassara*, a Thracian Greek word for fox, because of its very fox-like shape), and has a number of confusing popular names—the Ring-tailed Cat, Cacomistle, or Cacomixtle, which is really the Aztec Mexican name. Its coat is a rich, gingery, orange-brown color, darker on the mid-back but glistening with a golden sheen; it is very soft and dense. The undersides are white, the nose pink. The eyes are surrounded by dark brown "spectacles," and there are black patches on the side of the nose and at the base of the ears. The tail is very dark brown with seven broad white bands, is white-tipped and considerably more than half the length of the head and body, which is about fifteen inches. They make permanent nests in holes among rocks or in trees, and hunt small live food by night. In the tropics they also eat green nuts and quantities of tree snails and frogs. The average litter is four, born in late spring, and there seems to be a great preponderance of males.

C. THE COATI

This animal (*Nasua,* literally and most appropriately "the nosey one," Fig. 45a) belongs to a group of closely related species that has its headquarters in Central and South America, where they are known by a bewildering variety of names. Among these is the "coatimundi" whence the only English popular name. In Arizona, they are quite numerous in the Huachuca Mountains, and in a few other isolated areas and are called "Chulas." The fur is very hard and tan-brown in color; the claws are long, sharp, and directed forwards, the tail tapers but cannot be used for grasping things. The nose is rubbery and slightly upturned. Coatis travel in large tribes composed of all ages, and numbering up to a 100 individuals. They feed on all manner of animal and some vegetable food which they gather both in trees and on the ground.

5. THE WEASEL FAMILY

We now come to a large assemblage of small-to-medium animals most of which are individually well known but which, taken together, confuse all but the most stubborn enthusiasts. They are known collectively as the *Mustelidae* from the Latin name for the Weasel (*Mustela*) and are found throughout Eurasia, Africa, and the Americas, but the family can be sharply divided into a number of obvious groups, of which half a dozen, represented by no less than 60 distinct species, are found in North America—namely the Martens, Weasels, Wolverines, Skunks, Badgers, and Otters. Apart from the True Weasels, of which 24 North American species have been defined, they fall into a dozen quite easily distinguished types which include all the valuable fur-bearing animals like the Mink, Marten, etc. They can be grouped as follows:

A. MARTENS

These are large, arboreal weasels with moderately long, bushy tails. They inhabit the northern part of the continent—*i.e.* the great pine forests of Canada and the tongues of these forests which extend south *via* the mountains to California, New Mexico and Colorado in the West, and to Virginia in the East.

(1) The American Marten

Often erroneously called a Sable (which is quite a different species from Siberia) this species (*Martes americana*, see Fig. 46) is the American equivalent of the Pine or Baum Marten of Europe and the fur trade. It is a beautiful, rich, yellowish-brown color with dark brown limbs, tail and ears. The latter bear a white fringe. The undersides are slightly lighter and there is a light patch of various shapes, and pale ochre to orange in color, on the throat and fore-chest. The extended head and body of a large male measures about eighteen inches, and the tail, which is bushy, some eight inches. The face is sharp, the ears pricked and the expression alert. Inhabiting only the dense forests, Martens make a regular nest lined with leaves, grass, or other material in holes in trees in which up to four young are born in April.

GRIZZLY BEAR

RACCOON

OPOSSUM

MINK

WEASEL

MARTEN

OTTER

46

47

Martens

(2) The Fisher

This, also known as the Pekan or Pennant's Marten (*Martes pennanti*—Fig. 47) , is better known as the Fisher, not because it fishes but because it takes fish out of traps. It is also sometimes misleadingly known as the Black Fox. It measures up to three and a half feet of which sixteen inches is composed of a bushy, tapering tail, and can weigh up to a maximum of nearly 20 lbs. The color is very dark brown to black with some silver grizzling on the head, jowls, and shoulders. It is not so exclusively arboreal as the Marten, and hunts voles, hares and small deer on the ground, and regularly kills porcupines. It is, however, extremely agile in trees, and is known to catch there not only the nimble Red Squirrel but even the Marten. Like several other weasels it journeys continually around a regular range along which resting dens are dotted. In one of these, usually a nest in a hollow tree, up to four young are born in April after almost a year's gestation. The Pekan is now a Canadian forest animal, but still occurs in Maine and the Adirondacks, in the Rockies south to Montana, and on the Pacific coast from Washington to northern California.

B. TYPICAL WEASELS

There are two dozen typical members of the Weasel family in North America. These can be divided into nine recognizable groups of which two are very distinct and warrant separate names. These two inhabit the special environments of the open plains (The Black-footed Ferret) and the banks of lakes and streams (The Mink). The remainder, or True Weasels, vary considerably in size, color, and bodily proportions.

(1) True Weasels

To these are given the Latin name *Mustela*, which is compounded of the words *mus*, a "mouse," and *tolla*, from the verb *tollo,* meaning "to carry off": thus, the weasels are "those who carry off mice," than which there could not be a better description for they are our best allies in controlling rodent pests. They are long-bodied, short-legged, little predaceous hunters, all some color of brown from burnt umber to reddish on the uppersides, and either pure white, cream, or bright yellow below. There may be a distinct line of demarcation between the upper and undersides, or the colors may blend along the flanks, which are then often pronouncedly more reddish or even orange. The terminal portion of the tail is, except in some of the Least Weasels, always black, and in the Bridled and Western species the face bears a black or dark "mask" and other markings. Species inhabiting northern areas turn pure white, except for the black tail tip, in winter, when they are called "ermines," but there are intermediate areas where some change while others do not. The seven groups may be roughly summed up as follows: upon the tundras facing the arctic seas are found four medium-sized species with short, half-black, tails (Fig. 48). Two of these live on the extreme northern tip of Greenland north of the great ice cap. Next come four medium-sized, short-tailed species (Fig. 49) from the great northern pine forests of Canada and from the mountains. Then, to the south and east three large, long-tailed species (Fig. 50) inhabit the eastern states. On the great plains and in the Rockies are five medium to large species

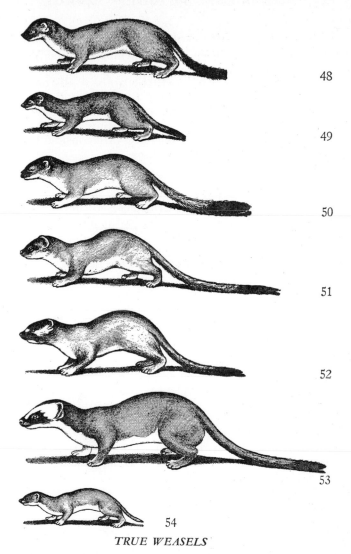

48

49

50

51

52

53

54

TRUE WEASELS

Fig. 48, Arctic Weasel (*Mustela arctica*); Fig. 49, Lesser (*M. cicognani*); Fig. 50, New York (*M. noveboracensis*); Fig. 51, Long-tailed (*M. longicauda*); Fig. 52, Californian (*M. xanthogenys*); Fig. 53, Bridled (*M. frenata*); Fig. 54, Least (*M. rixosa*).

(Fig. 51) with very long tails. To the southwest, in California, there is a distinct medium-long-tailed group (Fig. 52), while in Texas and New Mexico are found the subtropical Bridled Weasels (Fig. 53) which are very large with very long tails. In Canada and the northern mountain states there also occur the Least Weasels (Fig. 54), so tiny that they can pass through a hole the size of a "quarter," and which are on an average only seven inches long with one-inch tails. Weasels are ruthless hunters and

55

The Black-footed Ferret

often slaughter many times their food requirements. They often only suck the blood or the brains from their victims, but will also devour their flesh, bones, and even feathers. From four to eight young are born after a very long gestation period.

(2) The Black-footed Ferret

On the prairies from Montana to Texas lives a large weasel known as *Putorius nigripes,* or the black (*nigris*) foot (*pes*) with an awful stench (*putorius*). This is a true Polecat (see p. 63). The males, which are slightly larger than the females, grow to a length of two feet, of which about six inches is slender, tapering, furred tail. In color it is creamy yellowish-buff with a sprinkling of rich brown hairs above, while the underside is cream-colored. The forearms and paws, and lower legs and feet are black, and there is a dark brown band across the face enclosing the eyes like a mask. This agile creature feeds principally on Prairie Dogs (See page 99).

(3) The Mink

Though the name mink is now probably as well known as that of any other mammal, at least as a fur, few people know what the animal itself is like. It is a large water weasel with small ears, pointed muzzle, and rather short, tapering tail that is to be found throughout the continent from the arctic pine forests to Florida and the Gulf coast, and which is absent only from the more arid

56

The Mink

Southwest. The Mink constitutes a special subgroup of the weasels. It is known as *Lutreola* (the little), *lutra*, otter. It inhabits the banks of lakes, streams, and rivers, and even forages on the seashore and is as at home in the water as on land. Its food is a mixture of all the small land animals it can catch, frogs, fish, and insects, and at certain seasons when other food is scarce, various berries. Minks vary in size and general color from small and very dark in the Northeast, to very large and dark in the far West, medium-sized and light, almost to gingery in the South, and to very small and darker races in Florida. From four to eight and sometimes even twelve minute, naked, pink, blind, worm-like young smaller than your little finger are born in a nest in a bank or hollow log in mid-April. They are raised principally and sometimes solely by the mother and remain with her until August. They live alone except during the mating season and are extremely vicious and quite fearless creatures. They may still be found within the limits of some of our greatest cities, including New York.

C. THE WOLVERINE

The Latin name for the Wolverine, *Gulo luscus*, means literally *gulo*, "the swallowing thing" or "glutton," *luscus*, "who has gone blind," or as we would say, "The Blind Glutton." But although excessive gluttony and many dire and marvelous characteristics have been attributed to this animal, it is just a very large weasel with a corresponding quota of that boldness, strength, and resourcefulness common to the whole family. The Wolverine looks like a small bear with long, shaggy, dark brown fur, a short, bushy tail, and strong, semi-retractile claws.

57

The Wolverine

The muzzle and face are almost black, but the top of the head is light grayish-brown, and broad lighter bands extend from the shoulders along the flanks, and over the thighs to meet at the base of the tail. In bulk, Wolverines are the largest of the Weasel family, the head and body of large males reaching almost three feet, and weighing up to thirty-seven pounds. Neither bears nor the great cats molest them, and they in turn are strong enough to attack almost anything but these, including deer, reindeer, and even, it has been reported, the mighty moose. It has an evil reputation with woodsmen because it systematically plunders trap lines both of bait and catches, and often destroys the traps as well. It was always a northern animal ranging throughout Canada and is today very rare in the United States. Normally three or four young are born each year in an underground den in early summer.

D. SKUNKS

The skunks are an exclusively American tribe and are often misleadingly referred to as *polecats* (see p. 60) because of the overwhelming smell of the oil secreted by them in two sac-like glands under the skin at the base of their tails. This oil may be squirted at enemies. There are four distinct kinds of skunks in North America, divided among a score of species. Although they all vary much, both individually and racially, there is a simple rule for distinguishing three of these types; but the fourth constitutes a trap. One group of species, the Hog-nosed Skunks, have wholly white backs; the second, the Striped Skunks, have two dorso-lateral white stripes from neck to tail base; and the third, the Spotted Skunks, have four lines of elongated white spots. However, there is a fourth type closely related to the second group which may have a pure white back and which is known as the Hooded Skunk.

(1) Hog-nosed Skunks

These, *Conepatus* (see Fig. 58) are really South American Skunks whose range extends through Central America to just north of the Mexican border in Texas, Arizona, and New Mexico. They are rather badger-like with low bodies, short tails, and broad, naked, pig-like muzzles designed for burrowing and probing in earth, which they do more customarily than other skunks. The fur is coarse and thick, and the whole upper surfaces are white from the crown of the head to the tip of the tail. The face, throat, flanks and undersides are very dark brown to black and the underside of the tail is dirty-white with many hairs that are black at the base. The head and body measures about eighteen inches and the tail is a foot long. They are very solidly built, compact creatures. In some parts of South America the oil from these skunks is kept in little bottles which are unearthed when anyone is suffering from a severe headache. The resultant stench promotes sneezing and certainly appears to alleviate the symptoms of nasal catarrh. Like all the skunks, their food consists of a wide range of small animal life and vegetable food such as fruits and berries.

58

59

60

61

SKUNKS

BISON

BIGHORN SHEEP

MOUNTAIN GOAT

(2) The Hooded Skunk

This species, found in the extreme Southwest (Fig. 59), is really the Central American form of the next group—the Striped Skunks—together with which it may be distinguished from the previous group by the possession of 34 as opposed to 32 teeth, and by having a furred, un-pig-like muzzle. It is known to science as *Leucomitra* (i.e. the *leuco*, white, *mitra*, head-banded one) and may in some color phases closely resemble a Hog-nosed Skunk, the whole upperside being pure white. However, these skunks vary enormously in color pattern even in the same litter. Wholly black specimens occur with black or white, or black-and-white tails, and sometimes have two narrow white lines along the flanks. In habits they resemble the next species except that their young are born at the end of the rainy season.

(3) Striped Skunks

These are the common skunks of North America which are familiar to all by name if not by sight (see Fig. 60). Their latin name, *Mephitis*, was originally a Roman word denoting "any noxious, pestilential exhalation from the ground," but later became the name of a goddess whose sole occupation was to control such exhalations. These skunks are found throughout the continent except on the Arctic tundras, but they prefer open country or low growth to continuous forest areas, and they do not occur above the tree line on mountains or in the completely arid deserts. They not only thrive amongst, but seem to have an actual liking for humans and their habitations, often taking up quarters under barns and outhouses. They make large grass-lined nests either in the holes of other animals like badgers or woodchucks, or by digging themselves, and as many as a dozen of them may live together. The four to ten blind, helpless, little young are born in late April or early May after a 50-day gestation period, and are nursed for seven weeks before being taken out in a little procession led by the mother, and taught to forage. They start to hunt in the afternoon and are active throughout the night. In late fall they retire into their nests and sleep, living on a great accumulation of fat stored up during the summer, but do not truly hibernate. Warm winter days bring them out, but in February they become frantically energetic in searching for mates. In color these skunks are basically black with a greater or lesser amount of white in the form of, first, a narrow line down the middle of the forehead, second, a band across the back of the head, and third, bands or stripes of varying width that flow from this neck band along either side of the body to the base of the tail. The tail may be black, or white, or mixed in various ways, although all the individual hairs are white at the base. There are eight recognized species, in some of which the color pattern is fairly constant, while others vary bewilderingly even within a single litter.

(4) Spotted Skunks

These beautiful little mammals, *Spilogale* (Greek, *spilo*, spotted; *gale*, polecat) may be readily distinguished from all other skunks by the extreme silkiness, as opposed to harshness, of their fur, and by the more irregular arrangement of the white areas which always tend to form four stripes or bands down the length of the body (see Fig. 61). The white, however, forms in all manner of designs. The tail is almost always white-tipped. Although they reach almost the same dimensions as the striped skunks, they are much lighter animals. Also, their range is somewhat more southern, extending from Central America north to Puget Sound in the West, and Maryland in the East and in between roughly to a line drawn across the country between these two points. In habits they differ little from the striped skunks, but the whole breeding cycle is shifted backward so that the young are born at the end of winter. Like all skunks they make delightful, friendly, intelligent pets, even, as the writer can aver, when their musk glands have not been removed or closed. Skunks only use this dire defense in extreme emergency, though they threaten action often by raising their tails and advancing boldly upon their adversary, sometimes balanced on their front feet alone. When then do fire the fine acrid mist, it can be directed with great accuracy up to ten feet and, if it strikes the eyes, it is not only extremely painful, but may cause temporary or even permanent blindness.

E. THE BADGER

This mammal, *Taxidea taxus,* is seldom seen even in places where it is quite common, since it is extremely adept at concealment. It is a short-legged, very broad, solidly built animal clothed in a long, thick coarse coat, and armed with great claws on the forefeet for digging. In total length it may reach thirty inches, of which only about six inches is bushy tail. The skin is loose but tough, and the animal can literally take a beating such as no other creature of its size could withstand. The individual hairs of the pellage are gray at the base, then white,

62

The Badger

then black and tipped with silver, as may be seen from any shaving brush, for the manufacture of which they are still widely used. The general appearance is grizzled gray-brown. The facial markings are white and dark brown, and the feet are black. The Badger is an inhabitant of the open plains and prairies from Ohio and Michigan to Saskatchewan and Washington, and thence south to Texas, California, and Mexico. It is a prodigious digger, and can vanish underground almost before you can dismount from a horse. Its food consists of gophers, prairie dogs, and other rodents which it tunnels from their burrows, thus doing much good by keeping down these noxious pests. It digs large nests for itself at depths of up to 30 feet below the ground, in which a litter of up to five is born in May or June after an arrested gestation period of about ten months. The Badger is a fearless and rather ferocious animal that, if caught out in the open or away from its nearest burrow will turn upon man or beast, but although it can inflict a bad bite, its principal defense is retreat by digging.

F. OTTERS

The otters (*Lutra,* from the Latin) of North America constitute but a single species, although they are found throughout the continent from the Arctic Circle to Florida, the Gulf, and Mexico. Extremely dark, small forms occur on the cool, moist islands of Newfoundland and off the northwest coast. Otters are easily distinguishable, large, aquatic weasels, smooth dark-brown in color, with webbed feet and furry soles, and a long, tapering tail. They have a strong doggy smell, and are protected from extreme cold by a thick layer of fat under the skin so

63

The Otter

that they can remain in the water for long periods and swim below its surface for up to a quarter of a mile. Although living by water and making their dens in holes in banks, they travel long distances overland, especially in winter in search of open water where fish, which constitute their principal food, may be caught. They are also agile on land and a fighting match for almost any adversary. Yet, they are playful creatures and make very solicitous pets. In the wild they often construct slides on banks of snow or mud leading to water; down these, parties will toboggan for hours on their bellies with their forelegs tucked under them, apparently for the pure fun of the game. Two or three young are born in April or May and have to be taught to swim by their mother. In the South otters sometimes go fishing in saltwater creeks. Otters are reported to make a wide variety of noises, whistling, chirruping and barking not unlike a dog.

G. THE SEA OTTER

This, the most extraordinary of all the weasel family, is rather comically known to science as *Enhydra lutris*, which means simply "the otter otter," by the neat trick of latinizing the Greek word *enhydris,* and then mis-declining the Latin word *lutra.* However, it is the least otterish of otters, being exclusively marine, almost wholly aquatic, and very specialized in build with a long, four-foot, flattened, rather flabby body, short, thick tail, flat wide head with reduced ears, and very short, flipper-like limbs with the toes completely webbed. Its close, seal-like fur, which is one of the most coveted of all by the fur

The Sea Otter   64

trade, is rich dark brown sprinkled with silvery-gray hairs. These strange animals spend most of their time in the sea around rocky coves and promontories where there are extensive growths of seaweed between tidal levels. There they feed upon fish, crabs, shellfish, sea-urchins, and a certain amount of seaweed, diving, it is reported, to as deep as 300 feet. Floating on their backs, they use their broad chests as a table on which to hold and eat their food. Sea Otters used to dwell all along the Pacific coast from the Bering Straits to southern California, but were almost exterminated because of their valuable pelts. They are now closely protected and several colonies are coming back. Though sluggish, they are such adept swimmers that even their mortal enemies, such as the killer whales, find them hard to catch. One, or rarely two, young are born at a time.

IV. HOOFED MAMMALS

The hoofed mammals, which used to be known collectively as the *Ungulata* (Latin *ungula,* a hoof) are a composite group of ancient origin which, rather surprisingly, sprang from the same general stock as the *Carnivora*. Taken together they constitute the fourth largest group of living mammals, but they are clearly divided into four orders of unequal size—the little, rabbit-like Coneys or Hyraxes, the Elephants, and what are called the Perissodactyles and Artiodactyles, which mean in Greek simply the "odd-" (*perissos*) and "even-" (*artios*) toed (*dactylos*) ones. The former are the Horses, Tapirs, and Rhinoceroses, none of which are now found in North America. Thus all our hoofed animals have an even number of toes, and are represented by four of the nine living families of Artiodactyles, namely Oxen or Bovine Beasts, Deer, the Pronghorn, and the Peccary. The five families not occurring here are the Hippopotamuses, the true Pigs, the Camels, the Giraffes, and the little Chevrotains.

1. BOVINE BEASTS

This is a bewilderingly large family that often constitutes a great puzzle to the layman, for it contains not only the oxen, but also sheep, goats, goat-antelopes, antelopes, and gazelles. In America we have only oxen, sheep, and goat-antelopes. The so-called "antelopes" of the western prairies are not true antelopes which are confined to the Old World. Nor are they even of the Bovine group but constitute a family of their own, the *Antilocapridae* and should be called Pronghorns.

A. OXEN

Our oxen are two in number, the Bison and the Musk-ox, the latter being as its Latin name (*Ovibos*) implies intermediate between the sheep (*ovis*) and the true oxen (*bos*). Both were once in danger of extinction but the Bison has been saved, for it breeds well in captivity, and carefully protected herds have been built up in Canada, the West, and in Pennsylvania. Cattle introduced from Europe and Asia (see p. 156) have given rise to some extremely interesting feral breeds that have no counterpart elsewhere in the world.

(1) The Bison

Quite erroneously called a "buffalo," a name which
should be reserved for a quite different group of African
and Asiatic animals, this huge ox—measuring up to twelve
feet in overall length, standing six feet at the shoulder,
and sometimes, in large males, weighing well over a ton—
once roamed our prairie belt in numbers that could be
counted only in the millions. Before the coming of the
white man, herds ranged from what is now central Alberta to central Mexico, and from the Rockies to the
Alleghenies well east of the Mississippi. Today it is confined to zoos, parks, and reservations, except for a small
wild herd in a nearly inaccessible part of northern Can-

65

The Bison

ada. The bulls are considerably larger than the cows, and
bear a thicker, shaggier mantle of long fur on the head,
neck, shoulders, and front legs. The general color is a
slightly rufous dark brown, much darker brown on head
and shoulders. Usually only one calf is born per year.
There are two varieties of Bison, the prairie and the
woodland. The latter is the larger and browses on twigs,
leaves, and bark as well as grazing on grass like its prairie
relative. The only difference between Bison and the true
oxen, apart from their distinctive humped shoulders,
enormous broad heads, and small horns, is that they have
fourteen as opposed to the ox's thirteen pairs of ribs.
Bison steaks are little inferior to prime beef.

(2) The Muskox

This curious animal, although known from northern Eurasia in fossil form, is today an exclusively North American Arctic animal. It once ranged from the northern timberline to the Arctic Ocean, and from Greenland to Alaska, but today only one re-introduced herd remains in the latter, under government protection on Nunivak Island. It is slightly smaller than a domestic ox, with a very short (four-inch) tail, short, sturdy legs, a broad head with strangely downcurved horns that almost meet at their base on the forehead, forming a shield. They are clothed in a formless mass of long, shaggy, dark-brown

66

The Muskox

hair covering a dense, woolly undercoat. There are three distinct races, a brownish one with markedly white face on Greenland and the Canadian arctic islands, a very dark-colored variety from the western shores of Hudson's Bay to Great Slave Lake, and a third north and west of this between Coronation Inlet on the Arctic Ocean, and Great Bear Lake. Muskox do not breed until they are five years old, and then the females calve only once every other year, and twins are exceedingly rare. They live on the stunted growth of the tundra and in winter scrape away the snow to get at the scanty lichen that encrusts the rocks below. Certain Eskimos rely on their meat for sustenance, and they are preyed upon rather unsuccessfully by wolves, against which the males, with their deadly horns and stamping hooves, put up a very stout defense.

B. SHEEP

The wild sheep of North America present both the sportsman and the technical specialist with problems and confusions surpassing those encountered in studying any of our other large mammals, with the possible exception of the Dish-faced Bears. Despite their wide variety of size and color it has now been agreed that they are all contained in two species, *Ovis canadensis,* the Canadian, Mountain, Rocky Mountain, or Bighorn Sheep, and *Ovis dalli,* or Dall's Sheep. They have an enormous range from the Yukon, Alaska and its islands, to western Mexico, but their numbers have been greatly reduced, in some cases to the point of extinction, by introduced diseases, restriction of grazing ranges, and the ruthless and senseless trophy-hunting of the white man. The general population was always split up into a large number of distinct races, due principally to their preference for a mountain habitat. Each mountain range supported its own variety, and isolated ranges were often inhabited by very distinct types. They are all large, sturdy but sleek sheep with massive horns that curve backwards, then down and outwards, and finally, in old males, upwards again before the eyes. The rams usually exceed the ewes in bulk, being up to six feet in total length, with a six-inch tail, standing three feet six at the shoulder, and weighing up to 300 lbs. One or two young are born yearly in the spring, and immediately follow the flock as it moves about the precipitous slopes and crags between grazing fields. The food is that of typical sheep, but in some areas they will browse on bushes in the absence of good grazing. The range in color of Mountain Sheep is bewildering—from almost black to an overall cream white (Dall's Sheep of Alaska). However, the range of variation within the individual flock in some races sometimes almost equals that of the total color variation of the whole species. The typical coloration (Fig. 67) is grayish-brown above, slightly darker along the dorsal line, lighter on the flanks, and creamy-white below, with a dusky stain on the chest and inside the limbs. The hooves are black, and the rump bears a circular white patch. Southern specimens are

67

68

Wild Sheep

larger than northern, and Dall's Sheep of Alaska are al-together lighter in build and have smaller horns than the typical Rocky Mountain races. Darker races predominate on the moister Pacific slopes, but there is also an almost black form of Dall's Sheep, known popularly as Stone Sheep, which, as we have already noted, is normally white (Fig. 68). The horns are particularly massive, those of large males measuring up to three feet along the outside of the curve, and being as much as sixteen inches in girth at the base. The old belief that the horns were used as buffers on which the animal could land head first is quite false, but these animals can leap, or rather run, down perpendicular cliffs of enormous height, and some-times land by rolling over on soft ground below.

C. THE ROCKY MOUNTAIN GOAT-ANTELOPE

This rather ungainly, pure white animal is customarily called the Mountain Goat, but is really a quite distinct type of animal related to the Chamois. They are goat-like in build, and are covered with long hair forming leg coverings like the "plus-fours" golfers used to sport, and they even have pronounced goat-type beards. Both sexes bear small, upright horns that curve backwards at the tip. They inhabit the most precipitous upper slopes of mountains in Alaska, the Rockies, and the Cascades, where they meander about precipices that even normally

69

The Mountain Goat-Antelope

seem to invite suicide. But their hooves bear suction cups and will splay widely, and they are extremely sure-footed beasts. They travel in small parties, except in the spring when the males go off alone and the single or twin young are born in concealed crevices; these are tended by the mothers, and then assembled in small parties. Males grow to a length of six and a half feet, of which about six inches is tail, but stand almost four feet at the shoulder, and have been known to weigh up to 300 lbs. The Latin name, *Oreamnos*, from Oreas, a spirit of the high mountains, is particularly appropriate.

2. THE PRONGHORN

This unique animal is a relic of bygone ages that has survived on our western prairies and deserts from Alberta to Texas and Mexico, and west to southern and Lower California. It feeds on cactus, herbs, and bushes as well as grass, bears two young at a time, and once used to gather together in enormous herds during the winter. It is a small, slender, antelopine animal measuring about four and a half feet from nose to tail-tip, standing three feet at the shoulder, and weighing up to 125 lbs. In color it is light, sandy-brown with a small, dark-brown mane on the neck, yellow tan on the side of the face, neck, and flanks, and cream white below. The muzzle is dark brown

70

The Pronghorn

and there are dark streaks under the ears, and two white bands crossing the front of the upright neck. The hairs are pithy and full of tiny air pockets, and on the rump form a rosette of longer, sparkling white hairs which can be raised and spread at will by muscles under the skin. Most amazing of all, are the upright horns; these are hollow and borne upon a permanent bony core like those of oxen, but bear a small side branch and are shed each year, leaving the bony core covered with hard, black skin. They then grow back again, but from the tip downwards to the brow.

3. DEER

The Deer form a large family (*Cervidae*, from the Latin *cervus*, a stag) spread all over Eurasia, North America, and most of South America. They range in size from the mighty Moose to the tiny Pudu of the Chilean Andes which is about the size of a small terrier; they are found from the arctic wastes to the depth of equatorial forests. They are distinguished from other even-toed Ungulates by having branching horns or antlers—though some have simple, upright spikes, or even lack horns altogether—which are shed annually *in toto*, and then regrow under a thin-furred skin known as the "velvet." The horns are usually carried only by the males (see, however, p. 83). Most deer go about in herds and they can become so numerous in limited localities that they literally eat up all the winter feed they can reach, leading to mass starvation or emigration. In North America we have three distinct groups of deer, late comers from Eurasia, aboriginal indigenous forms, and an arctic series.

A. EURASIAN DEER

Two of our deer, the Moose and the Wapiti, are so similar to their Eurasian counterparts as to be almost indistinguishable from them. They appear to be comparatively new arrivals and only to have become established here in their present forms during the interglacial periods of the recent Ice Age. Most regrettably the animal we call the Moose is called the Elk in Europe, while we use this name for our representative of the Eurasian Red Deer. The latter would much better be called by its Amerindian name, the Wapiti.

(1) Wapiti

This large, handsome deer was once found all over the United States except in Florida, the Delta region, and the southwest deserts, and ranged far north into the Canadian forests. Today it has entirely gone from the east and central states and eastern Canada and is probably extinct on the lowlands of the Southwest except in one area in California where a small, short-legged, white-eared form clings to a precarious range. It is still, however, found

71

The Wapiti

throughout the Rockies from northern New Mexico and Arizona north to Montana, Alberta, and Saskatchewan. The coloration of the Wapiti is very distinctive, being lighter above than below, which is rather exceptional and doubtless protective for standing in forest clearings where the bright light comes from above. It is for the most part grayish-brown on back and flanks, but the underside is almost black, and the pronounced mane which clothes the whole neck is rich, dark brown. The face is lighter and there is a large yellowish rump patch. Males grow to almost ten feet and females to about seven feet in total length; the male stands five feet at the shoulder, and can weigh up to 1000 lbs. The antlers, which carry up to seven points and spread five feet, are used in terrific battles between the males in the rutting season. These battles are preceded by loud, roaring challenges. The young, born in late spring, bear white spots until the first fall moult. In the summer Wapiti tend to move up into the mountain pastures where they roam in small parties, but in winter they gather together in herds in the protected valleys. Rutting takes place in the fall, and the males are most solicitous of their crowd of females, for they are polygamous, throughout the winter.

72

The Moose

(2) The Moose

This is the largest of all deer, and can measure over
ten feet, stand almost eight feet at its humped shoulders,
and weigh up to almost a ton. The males carry enormous,
spreading antlers like upturned, open hands, which they
use for a variety of purposes. Primarily, they are what is
called secondary sexual adjuncts, but they are also used
for fighting in which the males often engage during the
rutting season with considerable determination and serious though seldom fatal results. In color Moose are an
even, very dark brown with lighter muzzles and legs. The
muzzle is swollen and overhanging, and there is a large,
furred, club-like appendage of skin called the "bell"
hanging from the throat. They inhabit the Canadian
forests to Alaska, but occur in the extreme northeastern
states and in the northern American Rockies. They prefer
the vicinity of lakes, and feed on water plants in summer,
often completely submerging for this food. For a few
weeks in September and October the males go about bel-
lowing for a mate, and may then be attracted by the
imitation of the female's answering call. The young are
born in May. It was recently estimated that there are still
at least 200,000 Moose in North America. In Europe they
have been driven in harness.

B. AMERICAN DEER

We have also in the New World a group or sub-family of medium to small, light-bodied deer which are quite distinct from all other members of the family. In North America these are represented by three groups of species, the White-tailed or Virginian Deer, the Black-tailed, and Mule Deer of the West. The others live in Central and South America. They are known to science as *Odocoileus* —i.e. the *koilos*, hollow, *odo*, toothed ones.

(1) White-tailed Deer

These (Fig. 73) are probably the best known and most often seen of our native wild animals, apart from rabbits and the Gray Squirrel (see p. 104), which infests even the parks in our largest cities. Thousands are killed in the hunting season, yet they have become so over-abundant in several areas in recent years that they have had to be declared pests for their own protection, lest they eliminate their natural food, and die of starvation or pestilence. They are slim, graceful animals, normally of gentle habits, that inhabit the wooded areas of our country from Oregon to Ontario, and thence south to New Mexico, Texas, Louisiana, and Florida. On the keys off southern Florida there are still some hundred examples left of a unique dwarf race three feet long, two feet tall, and weighing only about 50 lbs., which swim in the sea from key to key in search of fresh water and food. Virginian Deer are distinguished by having very large, white-lined ears, rather long—compared to all other deer —bushy tails, which are black above but with wide-spreading white fringes below; they have sleek, reddish-brown coats. Only the males bear antlers, which are without brow tines, and in which all the points are directed forward. The undersides and insides of the limbs are normally white. The bucks, which are slightly larger than the does, weigh up to 320 lbs., and measure six and one half feet overall, of which almost a foot is tail. Bucks may stand three and a half feet at the shoulder but as the head is carried high, the antlers can top six feet. The normal birth is twins, but one or three (the latter not triplets) are common. They are usually born in early

ELK OR WAPITI

WHITE–TAILED DEER

MULE DEER

73

74

75

AMERICAN DEER

summer, and are profusely spotted with white. The antlers are shed in the late fall and winter, and the new ones
begin to grow three weeks later, taking until the following September to reach full size. The bucks then rub off
the velvet, and engage in rather half-hearted contests
during the short rutting season.

(2) Mule Deer

This group of species is spread over the central part
of the continent east of the Rockies, being found from
Alberta and the Dakotas to Minnesota, and thence south
to Texas and northern Mexico. In winter they closely
resemble the White-tails, but in summer they adopt a
fawn-colored coat. They are, however, dark almost to
black below except on the insides of the legs, which are
white. The upper throat is also markedly white and
there is a pronounced circular rump-patch. The tail is
circular in section, naked below, and bears a black terminal tuft; it provides an easy means of distinguishing
the Mule Deer from both the white- and black-tailed species (see Figs. 73, 75, page 81). The head is larger in pro-
portion to the body, and is carried more erect than by the
White-tailed species. The body is heavy-set and compact.
The antlers are of wider spread and of distinctly different
construction.

(3) Black-tailed Deer

On the Pacific side of the western mountains from Sitka
in the north to Mexico in the south the Black-tailed Deer
replace the other species. These are smaller animals with
lighter bodies and small heads held erect. In color they
are not unlike the White-tailed species but there is less
white below, a distinct light throat patch, and a notable
difference both in the structure and color of the tail (see
Figs. page 81), which is carried hanging downwards. It
is white below and black above with the white forming a
marginal fringe. The antlers are of wider spread than in
the White-tailed deer. Full grown bucks seldom exceed
200 lbs. In a few areas their range overlaps that of the
Mule Deer, but they keep apart, the latter preferring
more open country. Two fawns are normal and are concealed by the mother who then lives apart from the buck.

C. REINDEER (*Caribou*)

The third group of deer are the Reindeer or Caribous (*Rangifer*) of which there are three distinct assemblages of closely related species in Canada, each with a distinctive distribution. However, the types blend to some extent along the belts where these assemblages meet. The typical reindeer, represented in America by the Barren Grounds Caribou, are arctic animals found only north of the great pine forests on the tundras that circle the pole in a wide strip from Lapland in northern Norway, *via* Russia and Siberia, Alaska and Canada to Greenland. They were domesticated in prehistoric times by the Lapps, Samoyedes, Tungus, Yakuts, and other inhabitants of these northern lands in the Old World, but not by the Eskimos in the New World. A small herd of domestic reindeer was imported into Alaska from Norway in 1892 and now numbers about 50,000. Although small deer, seldom exceeding six feet in length and standing only about three and a half feet at the shoulder, they can be ridden for miles on end, day after day, by men of normal weight, and have performed feats of endurance pulling loaded sledges that almost defy belief. They are called Reindeer because you can put reins on them. They can pull twice their own weight over snow continuously for two days. One pulled two Swedish officers at an average of 18 m.p.h. for 16 hours, and another made an 800 mile dash over the mountains of Norway in 49 hours, continuously running, and pulling an officer in a small sled to warn the King of a plot against the state. It dropped dead on arrival. In addition to their use as riding, pack, or draught animals, the Reindeer also has meat of high quality, the skins make fine leather that can be used with the fur on as clothing or as sled covers, while blankets can be woven from the woolly fur. The sinews make exceptionally strong cord, and the antlers are used to make all manner of small tools and instruments. The milk is so rich it has to be diluted by three times its volume with water, and from it cheeses, whey, and an alcoholic beverage can be made.

Both sexes bear horns which, in the males are very large, wide-spreading, and much, though irregularly,

76

77

78

REINDEER

branched; the branches form a number of small, hand-like expansions where they divide. The two brow tines extend forward low over the muzzle and one often has a palm-like expansion at its front end. Reindeer carry their heads forward and the body slopes only gently to the withers.

(1) Barren Grounds Caribou

The smallest species most closely allied to the Eurasian reindeer (see Fig. 76) was once found in enormous herds all over the tundra lands from Greenland, Labrador, and the Canadian Islands to Alaska, but is now considerably reduced in numbers. They have rather shaggy fur, longer in winter than in summer, somewhat of a throat mane, and very large, long, pointed hooves that clack together when they run. They are all light in color, a mixture of white, cream, gray, and various light browns, but are darker in summer with distinct light areas on the muzzle, about the base of the tail, and above the hooves. The arctic island races are so light they may be almost white; the Alaskan races are darker.

(2) Woodlands Caribou

These species (Fig. 77) are much larger, and inhabit the birch and pine forests of Canada and once were to be found in our northernmost states. They band together only in winter, and travel alone or in family parties the rest of the year. They are found only in the East from Great Slave Lake to Newfoundland and south almost to the U.S. boundary. The males are larger than the females, and can weigh up to 300 lbs. and stand over four feet at the shoulder. In color they are brown with yellowish neck and tail patch.

(3) Mountain Caribou

These great deer (Fig. 78), over eight feet long, standing over four feet at the shoulder and weighing up to 600 lbs., are inhabitants of the mountainous areas of the Yukon and the Canadian Rockies. They are very dark brown, sometimes almost black, in color, with immense splaying antlers. The neck, rump-patch, and undersides are grayish and always lighter.

4. THE PECCARY

Although pig-like in general form, the Peccaries (*Tayas-suidae*, from a South Amerindian name, *Tayassu*) are not true pigs (see p. 157) but a distinct family of tropical American animals. One species, the Collared Peccary, occurs in western Texas, southern New Mexico, and Arizona. They are ugly brutes about three feet long, of which a good third is head, and are clothed in coarse hairs banded black and yellowish-gray, giving a grizzled effect.

79

The Collared Peccary

The limbs are black, and there is a diffuse yellowish ring round the neck. The young are more truly pig-like and are covered with a much softer, rather fluffy, reddish-brown coat. Peccaries, in the tropics, travel about in bands, sometimes of several hundred, and although often seen on the open plains dotted with Opuntia cactus, they prefer the thickest cover possible. They will eat almost anything, animal or vegetable, alive or dead. They are normally very retiring beasts, but they can be most menacing, and very occasionally dangerous if molested. The author was treed by a large band for several hours in his pajamas right in camp in Nicaragua.

V. MAMMALS THAT LEAP

The hares, rabbits, and their little relatives, the Pikas or Whistling Hares, form the most compact and easily recognizable order of mammals. They are closely related to, and were for long associated with, the next order, the Mammals that Gnaw, under the general heading of *Rodentia,* but already at the dawn of the age of mammals 60 million years ago they were quite distinct, as we now know from their fossil skeletons discovered in rocks of that age. Today they are found all over Eurasia, Africa, and the Americas in suitable localities outside closed forrests, and they have been introduced into Australia and New Zealand, where they have become both a terrible pest and the foundation of a tremendous industry. Most of our felt hats are made of Australian rabbit fur.

1. HARES AND RABBITS

You can go quietly insane trying to figure out the difference between hares and rabbits. The original European Rabbit happens to be a rather unique and distinct animal that digs its own holes, and is quite unlike the European Hares. Thus to our ancestors there was no question as to which was which until they got to America where they found two dozen species varying from extreme, long-legged hares to little, toy-like rabbits, to which they gave all kinds of names like cottontails, jackrabbits, snowshoe rabbits, and so on, without any regard to the original distinctions between the long-legged, leaping hare, and the short-legged running rabbit. If, however, this simple distinction is borne in mind, little difficulty will be encountered in identifying the animals seen in the field or held in the hand.

A. HARES

Hares (*Lepus,* from the Latin for hare) are predominantly northern and western forms; they are absent from the wooded lowlands of the Central and Southeast, and the lower Mississippi Valley. They are larger than rabbits and have longer legs and usually longer ears. The species may be divided into five distinct groups, three of which are commonly called Jack-rabbits and inhabit the West.

(1) Arctic Hares

These form a distinct group that is always white with black-tipped ears in winter (see Fig. 80) and in one case (the Greenland Hare) is almost pure white in summer also. The others, of which there are half a dozen races extending from Newfoundland and Labrador to Alaska throughout the tundra north of the tree line, and on the Canadian islands, are all various combinations of brown and grayish-brown in summer, white below, and with white tails and sometimes also white feet. They are the largest hares in the continent, some measuring over two feet in length, having moderate ears about four inches long, and sometimes enormous hind feet measuring up to seven inches in length. They form the staple food of the larger arctic carnivorous birds and mammals. The size of the litters varies from year to year, gradually increasing until veritable swarm conditions obtain, and then dropping again suddenly.

(2) Varying Hares

Also ranging across Canada from Newfoundland to Alaska, thence south to the U. S. border, and down the western mountains to New Mexico, and also found throughout New England, and via the upper Alleghenies, to Virginia, is another group of large hares (Fig. 81) which, with the exception of one race on the lowlands of the state of Washington also turn white with black-tipped ears in winter. They also have enormous hind feet. They do not occur on the extreme open tundras bordering the Arctic Ocean nor on the Canadian islands or Greenland. They are known collectively as the Varying Hares, but in some areas one species or another is referred to as a Snowshoe Rabbit, or even as a Jack-rabbit. The hind legs are not excessively long and the ears are of only moderate length. In color they are in summer the usual gray-browns, browns, and brown-grays of most hares, but the underside is white. If you blow the soft fur apart, however, you will find it is slate-colored at the base all over the body. These hares on the eastern coastal lowlands are of a distinctly reddish shade in summer. The number of young and of litters per year is also cyclical, rising to a peak and then dropping again.

80

81

82

83

84

HARES

(3) White-tailed Jack-rabbits

These large, moderately long-eared, rather heavy-bodied hares with very long legs and large feet (Fig. 82) inhabit the prairies and uplands of the West from the Cascades and the Sierra Nevada to Iowa; they also live up the mountains in those regions almost to the snow-line. They are merely rather exaggerated forms of the Varying Hare adapted to life in open country where they seek safety in flight by means of terrific, sustained leaps of up to twenty feet. Their tails, which are rather long compared with those of other hares, are always prominently white, and the summer pellage is of the usual gray-browns, but always rather on the light side. In higher latitudes and on the upper slopes of high mountains they may also turn white in winter. Like other hares they rest in "hides" under grass clumps, and in these up to three litters of about four young may be born each year.

(4) Black-tailed Jack-rabbits

Clearly distinguishable from the last is another group of large, very long-legged, enormous-eared, leaping hares (Fig. 83) which have a jet black "dagger" extending from the lower rump to the middle of the upper side of the tail. The rest of the tail is gray, and the end third of the ears is black. They are found throughout the southwest desert areas from Oregon to Lower California, thence east to Nebraska and Texas, and south into the Mexican uplands. In some areas they mingle with White-tailed Jacks, but their greater speed and different method of jumping when in flight immediately single them out. They constitute a serious pest in the West, and have to be killed off in wholesale drives by shooting and poisoning. There are several litters of up to four young a year.

(5) White-sided Jack-rabbits

These (Fig. 84) are the most exaggerated of all Hares; they occur only in the extreme southern fringe of Arizona and New Mexico where they are sometimes called Antelope Jack-rabbits. They have immense legs and six-inch ears, and may be recognized by the light bands along the sides of their bodies from shoulder to rump.

B. RABBITS

In North America we have two distinct kinds of rabbits—the Cottontails (*Sylvilagus*) and the Pygmy Rabbit (*Brachylagus*). Unfortunately for the purists, *lagos* was the Greek word for "hare," while *sylvi* means "of the woods," and *brachy*, "short," referring to the length of leg. The confusion is thus complete, for our Cottontail Rabbits are technically known as Wood-Hares, and Short-legged Hares respectively. Although neither of them digs holes like the true European rabbits, they are compact, short-legged creatures that inhabit meadows, open areas in woods and forests, and, in the West, brush country. Rabbits are our commonest game animals, probably because of their wary habits and excellent protective coloration, and because they are very prolific. There are six distinct assemblages of Cottontails, as follows:

(1) Eastern Cottontails

These Cottontails measure about 14 inches, of which the tail accounts for some two inches. The hind legs, though longer than the front ones, are comparatively short, and the hind foot is only about three and a half inches long. The ears are quite short—only about two and a half inches long. In color they are the usual combinations of gray and gray-brown, but in the eastern varieties the nape of the neck is usually reddish, while the undersides are white except for a dusky suffusion on the throat. The most prominent feature is the tail, which is invariably pure white except for a small brown dagger above. This is concealed when the animal takes off, as the tail is then curled upwards. Their tails do, in fact, look just like cotton bolls. The typical Eastern Cottontails (Fig. 85) are found from Connecticut to Florida on the eastern seaboard, thence west, south of the Great Lakes to the Dakotas, Colorado, Kansas, Oklahoma, and Texas. There are odd, small and dark races on the islands off the east coast and in some isolated mountains. There is a distinct variety in New England, known as the Wood Rabbit, which has a pinkish coat covered with sparse black hairs, and a noticeable black patch between the ears extending down on to the forehead. The ears are very short.

(2) Western Cottontails

When dealing with common mammals of which there are a large number of species or varieties, it is the soundest rule for the layman to take a pencil and a map of North America, and mark out the areas from which each type or group has been reported. Normally, it will then be found that the animal you have caught or seen will be immediately identifiable simply because it is the only type of that animal which can be found in your area. Unfortunately, this is not so with the Cottontails, for throughout a considerable area in the West there are a variety of races of no less than three distinct rabbits known as the Western and Mountain Cottontails, and the Brush Rabbits. The first are distributed over a wide area from California to central Texas, and thence north via Colorado and Wyoming to Montana. To try to describe the way in which this species (*Sylvilagus auduboni*) differs from the Eastern Cottontails would be impossible in this compass, and therefore worthless. The species (Fig. 86) tends to grow to a large size for a Cottontail, has a big tail and small ears. It inhabits the lowland plains and valleys, and the arid deserts wherever there is sufficient cover, but where food is available it also spreads up the mountain slopes to considerable heights.

(3) Mountain Cottontails

Known also as Nuttall's Rabbit, this somewhat smaller, darker species with small ears (Fig. 87) is found from eastern Washington and Oregon to the western Dakotas and south to California and New Mexico. As its name implies, it is more prevalent in mountainous districts, being found in the pine forests at heights of many thousand feet in the Rockies. However, in some areas it is also reported down to sea level, and there mingles with Audubon's Cottontails. Mountain Cottontails are slightly smaller than Eastern, and much smaller than Western Cottontails. They are also darker gray-brown above with distinctly gray rumps, and reddish on the nape of the neck and limbs. Expert advice and a careful record of where the specimen was taken will, however, probably be needed to distinguish a single specimen of this species from the last.

85

86

87

88

89

90

RABBITS

(4) Brush Rabbits

This term presents certain difficulties, for the reddish tinged Eastern Cottontail of New England, the Wood Rabbit, is often also called by this name. However, we are here referring to a small species of cottontail (Fig. 88) with dark pellage and small tail and ears, that is to be found tucked away on the lowlands of the Pacific coast from Oregon to Lower California. In some places its range overlaps that of the Western Cottontails, but it prefers the thicker brush country, is noticeably smaller than that species, and is confined to the Pacific slope.

(5) The Marsh Rabbit

This species (*Sylvilagus palustris*, Fig. 89) is quite distinct from all the preceding and is confined to the lowlands of the southeast coast from the region of Norfolk, Virginia to the tip of Florida, and to the Gulf coast of Alabama as well as the numerous islands lying off these coasts. They are small and dark brown in color with little, delicate, reddish-colored feet, small, rounded ears, and a very short tail. The undersides are dirty gray-white but the tail is dusky below. They inhabit the thickest lush vegetation, notably on the "hummocks" that rise from the marshes, and there is evidence that they sometimes go swimming deliberately. Although they can also hop and bound, they customarily mince around more in the manner of small cats, and they make regular runs in and under the dense vegetation along which they move about only by night.

(6) The Swamp Rabbit

To the west of the range of the Marsh Rabbit—that is throughout Alabama and the Mississippi Valley lowlands north to Illinois and west to the eastern half of Texas together with the Gulf coast from Mobile to the Mexican border—is found the Swamp Rabbit (Fig. 90). This is a large, very sleek-furred rabbit with a large head and small tail. It is light buff in color, white below and has a white tail. It lives in the damp bottomlands rather than on the knolls, is more pronouncedly aquatic than the Marsh Rabbit, swims long distances, and even dives for food and to escape danger.

C. THE PYGMY RABBITS

In a limited area of upland plateaus covered with dense, low bushes, between the Rockies, the lowlands of Oregon and the uplands of Nevada and Utah, there is to be found the smallest of our rabbits, a little species distinct enough to be given a separate name (*Brachylagus*). It looks for all the world like a small Cottontail, but does not show a white signal tail. Pygmy Rabbits are the usual brownish-gray above, lighter on the flanks, and white below, but measure just under a foot in length, with a

91

The Pygmy Rabbit

tail less than an inch long. Although comparatively common in many parts of their restricted range they are still by no means well known even to zoologists. They are also very hard to catch because they live under the dense patches of bush which often extend over large areas and through which they dart from one to another when disturbed. Also, their coloration constitutes a perfect camouflage against the light, sere soil. Those who have studied this animal remark upon its habit, unique among American rabbits, of changing its coat completely in winter, when it develops a long, fluffy, pale reddish overcoat, a black edge to the ears, and a white fluff within them. These small rabbits do not dig holes as was once supposed, but they may, like the cottontails, take up residence in the abandoned burrows of other animals such as badgers. They are, however, very shy and retiring in habits and prefer to remain under the thickest bushes and other cover.

2. PIKAS

On the upper slopes of a score of mountain ranges in the West, from Alberta to New Mexico and down through the coastal ranges of Washington and Oregon, there may be found, and more often heard, the little, tailless Pikas or Conies, sometimes also called Whistling Hares, or Rock Rabbits. There is something ineffably delightful about these tiny, active bundles of fluff, more especially when they withdraw their heads and sit all bunched up and look like large, furry eggs. They are of various shades of stone brown, varying much even within small communities, and it has been given as an opinion that individual animals do not necessarily come out the same color after

92

The Pika

one or more molts. The feet and undersides are always lighter, even to pure white. They inhabit screes, dwelling together among the crevices between the jumble of rocks, wherein and whereupon they gather and pile up great stacks of vegetable cuttings which are neatly arranged to promote thorough drying, as in our haystacks. On this they feed, and they are most solicitous about its care, hauling it underground at the approach of storms, and dragging it out again to dry later. They bear three or four tiny, furry young in late spring deep in their rocky galleries. Pika colonies emit night and day an endless cacophony of high-pitched, keening whistles that seem to reverberate inside your head and which echo back and forth among the stones in a most eerie manner.

COTTONTAIL RABBIT

VARYING HARE OR SNOWSHOE RABBIT

WOODCHUCK

HOARY MARMOT

VI. MAMMALS THAT GNAW

The Mammals that Gnaw, or *Rodentia,* comprise more than half the number of living species, and almost a third of the known *genera* of mammals, and exceed all others put together in total numbers of individuals by thousands, tens of thousands, or perhaps even hundreds of thousands of times. There are 200,000 moose, and 175,000,000 human beings in North America, but every square mile of land from the arctic tundras and bleak mountaintops to subtropical swamps and completely arid deserts supports thousands of rodents, their numbers rising in times of "swarming" of a single species to as high as 12,000 per *acre* over large areas. Since the area of North America is 8,664,860 square miles, there are thus at least ten billion and probably nearer ten trillion rodents within its confines. There are no less than 30 families of rodents of which nine are found in North America, split up among 40 genera and over 300 species, yet it is unlikely that the average person will know a dozen of these by name. There is thus a vast host of small and obscure mammals living around and among us which are of the utmost economic importance but the identification of which taxes even the abilities of experts. Moreover, so many of these are so much alike externally that only detailed examination of their teeth and other anatomical features will serve to differentiate them. Within their own groups also they vary bewilderingly. It is therefore almost impossible to identify many of them in the field, and it is sometimes an equally hopeless task even when you have the creature in your hand.

All the rodents found in this country, however, have a place in the following pages, but how to identify them must frankly depend upon your individual keenness, patience, and fortitude.

1. SQUIRRELS

The family *Sciuridae* (from the Latin *sciurus* meaning "shade-tailed") contains many creatures that most people seldom ever think of as being in any way connected with the little arboreal animals we see in our woods and parks. In fact, most of them have other popular names.

A. MARMOTS

Better known to Americans as Woodchucks or Ground-hogs, these are simply large, short-tailed squirrels that live in holes in the ground. There are three distinct species—the northeastern Woodchuck, the western, Yellow-bellied Marmot, and the so-called Hoary Marmot of Alaska and the Northwest. The eastern Woodchuck is a brindled yellowish or reddish brown, lighter below and on the sides of the muzzle, and with dark brown forepaws and lower legs. Large males measure over two feet, of which six inches is tail. They are found from Labrador and Nova Scotia throughout New England and the central eastern states west to the Mississippi, and thence north *via* Minnesota and Central Canada to the

93

Woodchuck

northern Rockies. The Yellow-bellied Marmot is more pronouncedly brindled, and often bears a sort of cape of lighter fur over the rump. The undersides and lower limbs are strongly washed with yellow. They inhabit a block of territory from British Columbia to California, and east to the Dakotas and New Mexico. The Hoary Marmots are larger, and brindled black and white rather than brown and yellow. The undersides are usually whitish. They are found in the Canadian Rockies and Alaska. They live in loose communities high among the mountain screes. The eastern Ground-hog lives alone in holes and does well among human habitations. It hibernates for six months and seldom even puts in an appearance on Ground-hog Day, the 2nd of February, unless the weather is exceptionally mild.

B. GROUND SQUIRRELS

Scattered throughout the West from the Mississippi to the Pacific coast and from Alaska to Mexico are to be found five distinct genera of Ground Squirrels, comprising some forty species of which 25 belong to a single genus known as *Citellus* (the little, *citus,* quick ones) also misleadingly known as Gophers.

(1) Prairie-dogs

The *Cynomys* (*kyneos,* dog-like, *mys,* mouse, Fig. 94) is a small, plump but compact, short-tailed, sleek-furred, marmot-like rodent with small ears. It is found all over the prairies from Montana to Arizona and North Dakota to Texas. They are a slightly grizzled reddish sandy-brown above and buff below. There are two kinds, a plains form with a white-tipped tail, and a mountain form with dark facial markings and a larger, black-tipped tail. They are sociable animals, living in large communities or "towns" wherein their low, volcano-shaped burrow-entrances dot the open ground sometimes for miles on end. Towns up to 25,000 square miles in extent, and containing hundreds of millions of inhabitants have been described. The animals feed on the grass between their burrows. They have up to eight young in May. When approached, they give piercing alarm whistles and pop into their holes, but then watch your every movement by peering over the rim.

(2) Antelope Ground Squirrels

Ammospermophilus (the prolific one, *spermophilos,* of sandy places, *ammo*—Fig. 95) constitutes a distinct and readily recognized group of small (eight-inch) grayish-brown, gingery, or gray squirrels with small ears, white underside, and a single, pronounced white stripe extending from the ear along the flanks to the base of the tail, and sometimes also from the nose over the eye to the ear. Still more distinctive are their short tails, which are carried curved up over the rump like rabbits, and which are, except in one species, pure white below and black-tipped. They live in the driest places, are very inquisitive, and sit upright like the Prairie-dogs; they live in holes among rocks and whistle, chirrup, and trill.

GROUND SQUIRRELS

(3) Mantled Ground Squirrels

Callospermophilus (the *kallo,* beautifully adorned, prolific one, Fig. 96) is somewhat more "squirrel-like," with a slightly bushy, trailing tail almost half as long as the head and body. They are larger (seven inches, with five-inch tail), heavier in build, and they utter typical squirrel-like churrings and chirrupings. In color they are very distinctive, having bright orange head, neck, shoulders and forelegs, with light rings around the eyes, and a spot behind the ears. The rest of the body varies from brindled yellowish gray-brown, to deep chestnut, or olive brown, but along the upper flanks from shoulder to thigh are bright white bands bordered above and below by black bands. The undersides are whitish-yellow, and the tail, which is flattened horizontally, is brindled dark brown and ochre above, and buff below, with a black band running around the periphery halfway along the hairs. They live in holes and are found from British Columbia to California, Arizona and New Mexico, mostly in woods on the mountains.

(4) True Ground Squirrels

The two dozen species of Gophers or True Ground Squirrels (*Citellus*) range all over the West from Hudson's Bay and the Mississippi to Alaska, Mexico and the Pacific Coast. In general they are rather heavy-bodied, short-legged squirrels with tails between a quarter and a third of their total length, and with small, rounded ears placed rather low on the head. Most, but not all, have hard fur that in southern forms may be sparse and almost spiny. They have rather large claws, and dig their own holes; they do not climb trees, and most of them live in country that is treeless. Except in the hot southwestern desert region, they hibernate for long periods, and in the North for more than half the year, living on an accumulation of fat stored in the body during the summer. They are very prolific, having a yearly litter of up to a dozen young. They are very conspicuous little beasts because they like stumps, knolls, and other prominent places upon which to sit or stand while peering around and uttering short, piercing whistles and trills to which they keep time with flicks of the tail. The best way to sort out the species is by a combination of geography, habitat, and appearance. Thus there are arctic, mountain, prairie and desert groups, and large and small forms in brush country. The arctic species (Hudson's Bay Ground Squirrel, Fig. 97) are large and short-tailed. They occur from Hudson's Bay to Alaska throughout the barren grounds. They are grizzled yellowish-brown above with irregular gray spots, more reddish on the head, and yellowish below. The mountain forms (Columbian Ground Squirrel, Fig. 98), found in the Rockies, are grizzled yellowish-gray above, orange below. On the brush-covered plains and uplands from Saskatchewan to California, but not on grass prairies, there occur two distinct types, both markedly gray as opposed to yellow-brown in basic color. The first group (Flickertails, Fig. 99) are medium-sized with moderately long tails; the second Little Gray Ground Squirrels (Fig. 100) are very small with short tails. Both have noticeably softer fur, the latter very soft. The tails are grizzled gray, black, and white, and the undersides are buff. On the prairies occur the most distinct group of all, most of which are very remarkably colored. The whole body is longitudinally striped with dark brown and white, but in the dark brown stripes are even lines of white spots (Fig. 101). The sides of the head, throat, forearms, lower flanks, and undersides are usually some shade of creamy-buff, and the tails are brindled buff and black. The desert forms (Spotted Ground Squirrels, Fig. 102) are of various colors but usually dappled with lighter spots all over the upperside, and plain light cream-colored below. Some of these, confined to California, have longer tails which are round in section as opposed to the flattened form of all the other species.

(5) The Rock Squirrel

The *Otospermophilus* (*oto,* eared, Fig. 103) is a large (10-inch) long-tailed (8-inch), typical squirrel with upright, pointed and furred ears. It is dappled grayish-brown above, whitish-buff below, and the bushy, flattened tail is brindled gray, cream, and white. They are found from British Columbia to Texas, California and Mexico, and prefer rocky slopes and broken country. They whistle loudly in half a dozen descending notes.

C. CHIPMUNKS

More than a dozen species of these little, distinctive, striped ground squirrels (known as *Eutamias* and *Tamias,* meaning literally "one who cuts up and distributes") are now recognized. They are found throughout the United States except on the lowlands of the Southeast, from North Carolina to the Mississippi, and thence southeast to Florida. There is a single eastern species which ranges to Oklahoma; all the rest belong to a separate western genus called *Eutamias.* They all have more or less the same color pattern but vary widely in actual colors and in intensity and development of this pattern. The basic color may be greenish-olive, or various gray, yellowish, or rusty browns, always brindled with black

104

Chipmunk

and yellow. The undersides are usually lighter even to white, and rump and flanks may be orange or reddish. The moderately long tail is a darker extension of the basic color. The eye is enclosed in a dark nose-to-ear stripe, and above and below this are light stripes. There is a light spot behind the ears. Down the back from the crown to the tail base is a black stripe, on either side of this a band of the basic color, then a conspicuous black stripe, then a very light to white one, and below this another dark stripe. The last three fade out on shoulders and rump. Chipmunks live in holes in the ground where, in the East and North, they hibernate. They can climb to collect food which they carry to their nests in their large cheek-pouches for storage.

D. TREE SQUIRRELS

There are a dozen distinct species of tree squirrels in North America, all of which are assigned to the genus *Sciurus,* with the exception of the Red Squirrels (*Tamiasciurus*). They can be divided into four groups.

(1) Red Squirrels

Chickarees (Fig. 105) are found from Alaska to Quebec, and south via the Alleghenies to the Carolinas in the East, and via the Rockies to Arizona and New Mexico in the West. There are northern, western, and southwestern species, but they are all much alike and easily recognized, being much smaller than other squirrels and always of some rusty reddish color with either white, gray, or clear red undersides. They are compact in body, with short muzzles and upright ears which in winter bear a small pointed fringe of long hairs. The eyes are invariably ringed by a light area, and the tail is rather short and bushy, but widely flattened. The summer and winter coats are notably different, the former usually being much lighter and brighter, and in many forms an intense black line is then developed on the flanks at the junction of the upper and underside colorations. They inhabit the northern pine forests, spend some time on the ground and often make food stores in holes, but build their nests either in forks of branches or in holes in trees. They do not hibernate, and four or five young are born in late spring.

(2) Gray Squirrels

There are distinct eastern and western groups of these, the former ranging from the St. Lawrence to Florida, and west to Minnesota and Louisiana; the latter is found only along the Pacific slopes from Washington to Mexico. The western species have much larger, wider tails, and spend more time on the ground. Both build large nests of leaves and twigs on the branches or in holes in trees. In these, one or two litters of three to six young are produced each year. They are brindled gray, lighter below, and washed with yellowish, the hairs being black-banded and tipped with white. Gray Squirrels are probably our best known native mammals (see Fig. 106).

Tree Squirrels

(3) Fox Squirrels

These are the largest of our tree squirrels, Fig. 107. There are a dozen most distinct varieties all of which vary bewilderingly in color and color pattern. They are a southern form, ranging from Mexico to Wisconsin *via* the Mississippi Valley, and up the east coast from Florida to Pennsylvania. There are often gray, yellowish-fawn, and almost black phases in the same locality, while some races have white muzzles, ears, and feet. Their tails may be either dark or light with light fringe.

(4) Tuft-eared Squirrels

In a small triangle between the Grand Canyon, the mountains of central Colorado, and the borders of Arizona, New Mexico, and Mexico, but only in the mountain pine forests, are found the most distinguished of our squirrels, Fig. 108. They have huge, bushy tails, and tall, pointed ears adorned with long plumes or tufts. They are beautifully colored: brindled gray, usually with a broad red band down the back, black ear plumes, a black stripe on the flanks, and are either black or white below, with white feet. The tail is either stippled black and white, or pure white above, and is invariably white below.

E. FLYING SQUIRRELS

There are two distinct species of these wonderful little animals (*Glaucomys*, literally, *glaucus*, the blue-gray, *mys*, mouse) in North America, a small one found from New Hampshire to Florida and west to Minnesota and Texas, and a larger species found throughout the northern coniferous forests, in the Rockies, and on the Pacific coast. These are the most completely arboreal and the only nocturnal North American squirrels. They are small, nine to twelve inches, of which the large, flattened, paddle-shaped tail accounts for from four to five inches, and they have extremely soft, silky fur. Thin extensions of double, furred skin extend from the wrists to the ankles, partially supported by long strips of cartilage which grow

109

Flying Squirrel

backwards from the wrists. When the animal "spread-eagles" in leaps between trees, these skin flaps open like a kite so that the squirrel can glide on the air and make prodigious "flights."

The general appearance of these animals is chinchilla-like with pearl gray fur above washed with a pinkish or olive suffusion, and white below, but there is much variation and they are sometimes almost olive brown above and yellow below. The eyes are very large and black, and the ears small. Three to six young are born once a year in nests in holes in trees. Flying Squirrels eat a lot of insects and other animal food, as well as nuts, fruits, and some leaves and bark.

2. BEAVER

The half-dozen species of beaver, once scattered over the whole temperate and subarctic regions of Eurasia and North America, form the sole genus of a special family of rodents known as the *Castoridae* (from the Latin name *castor* which meant literally "the exceller"). Today they are rare in Asia, almost extinct in Europe, and greatly reduced in numbers in America, though they are coming back here rapidly because of protection, general public enlightenment, and changes in fur fashions.

110

Beaver

A. AMERICAN BEAVER

Beaver have, from the historical point of view, undoubtedly played a more important part in the history of North America than any other animal, the Sperm Whale (see p. 148) not excluded. Their contribution is two-fold. First, they have, as everybody knows, the unique habit of building dams in order to create ponds in which their "lodges" may be built for the rearing of young, and under which stores of winter food in the form of cut sticks can be accumulated and anchored in the bottom mud. This habit, carried on for thousands, perhaps tens of

thousands of years since the last retreat of the ice cap, re-
sulted in the formation of millions of square miles of
highly fertile meadows created by the silting up of these
ponds, the resultant raising of the water table, the
"swamping" of coniferous trees, and the opening of areas
marginal to the ponds to grass and broad-leafed vegetation. When a beaver pond silts up, the animals have to
move to another area and build another dam. Secondly,
it was the fine-furred pelt of the beaver, needed principally for men's hats, that first prompted trappers to
penetrate the wilds of the North and West, and in their
tracks came settlers, and ultimately roads and civilization.
Thus, beaver actually created an appreciable percentage
of our most fertile land, and later prompted the explora-
tion and exploitation of the country. Beaver are the
largest of our rodents, measuring up to four feet, of
which some eighteen inches is a naked, scaly, paddle-
shaped tail, four to five inches wide, which is used as a
propeller by rapid up-and-down strokes combined with a
sculling motion. They are heavy-bodied, hump-backed
creatures with squirrel-shaped heads, small ears, and extremely dexterous forefeet proportioned almost like human hands, though with long digging claws. In color they
are rich dark brown somewhat lighter below, and the
naked tail is steel gray. The fingers and toes are completely webbed, and the claw of the second toe is cleft.
Two to eight young, called "kittens" are born in spring
and are carefully looked after by their parents for at least
a year. In Newfoundland there is a small species distinguished by pronounced anatomical differences. They not
only indulge in cooperative tree-felling and the building
of dams with complicated sluices, but they also display
other qualities that can only be described as closely akin
to what we call "intelligence." They seem to know things
we do not, such as the height to which spring floods will
rise nine months later. They have a regular tribal or-
ganization, and work together as a community for the
benefit of the whole group. However, careful observations
made over a long period on captive beaver have demon-
strated that their urge to work is of a purely mechanical
nature and still laboriously carried out even when its ob-
jectives are unattainable.

3. MOUNTAIN BEAVER

Another rodent, found only in the Pacific coastal region of North America, and of which there is but a single species, and thus a single genus, also constitutes a special family of mammals that gnaw, known as the *Aplodontiidae* (the *aplöos*, or simple-toothed ones, referring to the cheek-teeth which have no roots at all). Despite its popular name it is no close relative of the Beaver, and is better known by its Amerindian name of the Sewellel. It is a very primitive creature left over from a bygone age.

A. THE SEWELLEL

This curious little burrowing rodent, virtually tailless, short-legged, small-eyed, hard-furred, and retiring, is

Sewellel

found only in certain areas on the Pacific coast between Puget Sound and central California, and along a narrow belt of territory down the Cascades and the Sierra Nevada. It is of a uniform, drab brown color, slightly darker along the mid-back, and lighter below, relieved only by a small white patch behind the ears. In summer the coat is somewhat lighter and even sandy. Sewellels are a little over a foot long. They live in large communal burrows or warrens, often near water, in which they swim with aplomb. Sometimes their underground workings are filled with water. Those found in the Sierra Nevada are distinctly larger and more wholly aquatic. Their food is leaves, succulent plants, and other herbage.

4. VOLES

Considerably more than half the rodents in the world are members of two enormous families known to zoologists as those of the *Muridae* and the *Cricetidae,* meaning literally that of the *mures* or mice, and the *krisos* or squeaking ones. This would at first sight appear to be a rather ambiguous statement, since by no means all the members of either family are mice, though many of both are, and they almost all squeak. However, there are valid anatomical reasons for differentiating them, notably a lack of roots to the teeth of most of the Cricetids which appear to be somewhat more primitive as a whole. The *Muridae* are an Old World family represented in North America only by the introduced House Mouse, and the Black and Brown Rats (see page 160). The Cricetids are predominantly American, but have representatives in other parts of the world. They are divided into two groups, the Voles and what we call Native Rats and Mice, to distinguish them from the True Rats and Mice, or *Muridae.* The Voles include the Lemmings, the Typical Voles, and the Water Rats.

A. LEMMINGS

Almost everybody has heard of Lemmings because of the widespread fable that millions of them every so often go marching down from the mountains of Norway to commit mass suicide in the North Atlantic. This idiotic story has just enough truth in it to keep it alive in popular fancy. What actually happens is that certain mountain populations of lemmings increase over the years at an accelerated rate due to the production of ever larger litters ever more frequently, until swarm conditions occur, and the food supply completely gives out. Then the whole host begins to move outwards in search of food, but still breeding all the time. They finally reach the lowlands. As many go away from as towards the Atlantic, and very few ever reach the latter, for they die off from disease and other causes on the way, or are drowned crossing the fjords that dissect the entire Norwegian coast. North American Lemmings also swarm, and sometimes in doing so they encounter lakes or arms of the sea in which countless thousands perish.

(1) Common Lemmings

These little six-inch, virtually tailless rodents (*Lemmus*, Fig. 112) live on the arctic tundra north of the forests from Hudson's Bay west to Alaska, and one species lives above the tree line on the Canadian Rockies. The ears are small and pressed close to the head under the fur, and the front feet are large with big claws for digging. In color they are various drab grayish browns, the lower back and rump often somewhat reddish; the undersides are lighter and washed with buffy-yellow. They feed on the tender parts of grasses, mosses, and lichens, and make extensive runways under this low, matted vegetation. They also dig endless interconnected burrows. The females bear eight teats, and large litters are born in early summer, but the breeding rate rises from year to year, and then, after swarming, pestilence, or mass emigration, drops off to a low ebb among the few remnants of the race left in the area.

(2) Collared Lemmings

Also known as Arctic Lemmings (Fig. 113) these are found all round the Arctic Ocean throughout the tundras of both the Old and New Worlds. Thus, in America they range from Alaska to Labrador and eastern Greenland. Their Latin name, *Dicrostonyx* (the ones with *dikros*, forked, *stonyxos*, claws) refers to one of their unique characters, that of growing a second huge claw under the normal claws of the third and fourth digits of the forefeet each winter, and then shedding them each spring. Another characteristic unique among all rodents, is that these lemmings, which are brownish-gray above and yellowish-white below, often with a bright rufous wash on throat and forequarters in summer, turn pure white all over in winter. A third oddity is that the external ears which are reduced to mere ridges under the long, thick, silky fur can be closed individually by a brush of stiff hairs controlled by muscles in front of the ear passage. They are active on the surface in summer, but in winter construct miles of passages below the snow and indulge in periods of partial hibernation. The double winter claws have something to do with the excavation of the snow.

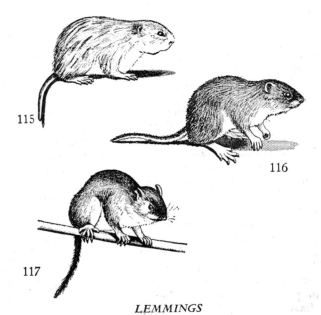

LEMMINGS

FLYING SQUIRREL

RED SQUIRREL OR CHIKAREE

JUMPING MOUSE

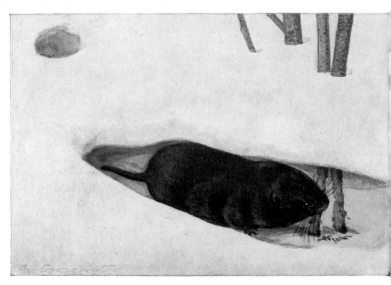

MEADOW MOUSE

(3) Bog Lemmings

The *Synaptomys* (*synapto*, joined together, referring to the arrangement of their cheek teeth, Fig. 114) bridge the gap between the lemmings and the typical voles. They are small, five-inch rodents with tiny half-inch tails; they prefer damp and boggy places, and are found throughout an enormous area, but mostly within the forests from Labrador to Alaska, and south via the mountains to a line drawn from central Washington to Virginia. They are communal beasts, living in small colonies in runways under the grass or moss, or in the surface mold of the forest floor. The color is a grizzled brown, gray, black, and yellow above, and silvery-gray below. The tiny tail is dark brown above, and white below. They apparently bear several litters of four to six young in nests lined with grass or sometimes with fur, and placed a few inches underground, but they keep breeding all year. The "thumb" bears a comparatively broad, flat, square-ended, digging claw.

(4) Mouse Lemmings

These variable and abundant little rodents known to zoologists as *Phenacomys* (*phenax*, an impostor, because some of them look quite unlike a vole of any kind) are spread all over the forested parts of Canada from Labrador to the Yukon, but not to Alaska, down the Pacific coast to California, and via the Rockies to New Mexico. They come in three "lines"; vole-like, terrestrial forms with short tails, longish fur, and small ears (Fig. 115); a larger, long-tailed, ground-living form of darker color on the Pacific Coast (Fig. 116); and a long-tailed tree-dwelling form in the same area (Fig. 117). They are believed to represent the remnants of those animals from which both the Lemmings and the true voles sprang. They are undistinguished-looking little rodents, colored various browns and gray-browns above, and white below. The tails are well furred. The ground-living forms are indistinguishable from the common Field Voles, and live in a variety of habitats—on the floor of the forests, in low vegetation covering forest clearings, and in the banks of streams. The arboreal species build nests of leaves and twigs in pine trees at some height.

B. TYPICAL VOLES

The typical voles constitute the next step on the way from the bunch-bodied, apparently earless and tailless lemmings, towards the more general concept of true "mousiness." As a whole they have prominent tails and noticeable ears; they are slenderer and somewhat longer-legged. There are three distinct groups of typical voles—the Field Voles together with the Short-tailed Field Voles, the Pine-Voles, and the Red-backed Voles.

(1) Field Voles

Also known as Field Mice or Meadow Voles (*Microtus,* Fig. 118), these are really our commonest mammals, probably surpassing all others (even the White-footed Mice, see p. 120) in actual numbers of living individuals. Detailed studies of their true abundance have brought to light some astonishing facts. About 50 species are now recognized, inhabiting almost every type of land from the arctic tundras to the hot deserts of the Southwest, and from coastal marshes to the bare tops of mountains throughout the whole continent. They make nests of grass either on the surface or in shallow burrows, and construct endless runways under the surface vegetation; these they keep clear and free by cropping all sprouts that may grow up in their paths. They are communal animals, but each one apparently maintains its own range of runways which cover on an average about the area of a tennis court. However, these little territories overlap so that very large numbers of individuals are packed into a small area. There is a regular population cycle which customarily reaches a peak every three to four years, when it has been estimated there may be up to 200 Field Voles per acre. There is also, however, a longer super-cycle during which the numbers may suddenly rise to 500, 1500, or even, as in the early part of this century in the Southwest, to 12,000 per acre. At such times the whole population may attempt to emigrate. They can do an enormous amount of damage by chiseling the bark off the stems of fruit trees, and by cutting down as much as 30% of various grain crops. They are small rodents up to six inches in total length of which some two inches is tail, with small feet, noticeable ears, and compact bodies. In color they

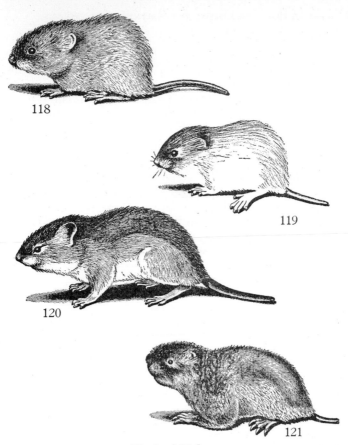

Typical Voles

are various browns from olivaceous to chestnut, chocolate, or even sandy shades, with narrow, lighter undersides, usually of some gray tone, but the variations dis-
played by their numerous races are almost unlimited.
They are very cleanly little animals that set up communal
toilets along their runways where piles of their little
green, pellet-like droppings are deposited. In the runways
also may be found strange little piles of neatly cut and
stacked collections of grass stems. These are created when
a stem is cut and hauled down to get at the seed-head.

Four to ten young are born at a time after a gestation period of three weeks, but the young are weaned in two weeks and the females actually start to breed when only three weeks old. Moreover, they have litter after litter from early spring to late fall, and sometimes go on all year. An oft-quoted case of one pair in captivity having 17 litters in one year, and one of the daughters herself having 13 in her first year gives some idea of their potential.

(2) Short-tailed Field Voles

In certain areas in the West from Washington to Nevada and California, a group of pale-colored field voles with very short tails (Fig. 119) have been separated from the common species as a distinct genus (*Lagurus*, the "little hares," *lagos*). Their habits are similar to the other voles which may sometimes live in the same area, but they remain apart. They are pale buff-gray above, and silvery-gray to white below, with very light gray feet and almost white tails. They occur mostly in scrub-zones between brush country and prairies.

(3) Pine Voles

These small (they average about five inches), short-headed, dark brown to russet or almost wine-colored voles (*Pitymys: pitys,* pine; *mys,* mouse, Fig. 120) are quite distinct animals of generally mole-like appearance and habits. Their tails are very short, not over an inch in length, and the fur is short, thick, dense, and glossy. They appear to be confined to the central and southeastern area from northern Vermont to Florida and thence west via the Appalachians and the Mississippi Valley to Iowa and Louisiana. They may be found in forest clearings and in woods with a ground cover of low growth. Their runways are regular tunnels in the earth, not on its surface. They are, however, very adaptable, and infest crop fields and market gardens. Just about the only habitat they shun is pine forests. They are root and bulb eaters, and in some areas a great pest. The breeding season continues for many months, and sometimes throughout the year. The young are weaned in about two weeks and ready to breed in two months.

(4) Red-backed Voles

The members of this genus (*Clethrionomys*, the mice with *klethron*, meaning "bolts," referring to peculiarities of the structure of their teeth) are the most typically "mousy" of all the voles (Fig. 121), having more pronounced ears and generally lighter build; their tails, though still short, bear a well-defined terminal brush of hairs, and are well-clothed; the eyes are larger than in Field Voles. There are five toes on fore and hind feet, but the thumb is very reduced and bears a small nail instead of a claw. They are northern animals occurring on the tundras and throughout the great boreal forest belt, south into lower temperate latitudes via the mountains, thus to South Carolina in the East, and to Colorado in the West. They are not, however, found on Greenland, the Canadian Islands, or Newfoundland. The fur is dense, long, and soft in winter, shorter and harsher in summer. The majority of species and races may immediately be distinguished from the Field Voles by a broad, reddish-colored band extending down the mid-back from the crown to the tail base, and encroaching on to the flanks to a greater or lesser extent. At some seasons some species, and in some localities other species, are very brightly-colored with the back bright red, the flanks orange ochre, and the undersides whitewashed with cream. There are, however, some races which completely lack the red back-band, and which otherwise look exactly like some Field Voles. Red-backed Voles are essentially forest animals, and they do not live in communities or construct runways. They wander about the surface, and travel by mole and shrew burrows under the leaf mold. Nor do they hibernate, and in the North they tunnel under the snow and remain active all year, living for the most part on food stores accumulated below ground in the fall. They start to breed in mid-winter and keep at it till fall; the litters average five, and follow each other at about three-week intervals. They are often active by day as well as night, and they cover considerable distances, for their size, in search of food. They can climb fairly well, and lay in large stores of vegetable food for the winter.

C. WATER RATS

There are two very distinct voles in North America that are of large size, and which have adopted an aquatic habit.

(1)   The Florida Water-rat

This animal is a little over a foot long, of which five inches is naked, scaly tail. The eyes are small and the external ears are inconspicuous. The forefeet are rather large and hand-like, the hind feet slender and partly webbed. There are two races, one spread all over Florida from the Okefenokee swamps of southern Georgia to the Everglades, the other confined to a narrow strip of swamps on the central east coast and keys and islands off that coast. It is known as the Water-rat, or *Neofiber al-*

122

Florida Water-rat

leni (Allen's *neo*, new, *fiber*, beaver). They live in the sodden masses of partially decayed swamp vegetation in both freshwater and brackish lagoons, lakes, and "slews," which are sometimes quivering, water-filled blankets lying on a sand bottom or actually floating on the water. In these the Water-rat constructs tunnel-like runways and capacious circular nests with dual entrances just above the water level. It also builds feeding platforms just above the water level by always hauling its succulent green food to the same place and leaving what it does not eat to decay on top of the mound. It has a waterproof, dark brown pelt with buff to white undersides.

(2) The Muskrat

This is our most important fur-bearing animal, and is to be found almost throughout the continent in suitable localities. It is absent from the driest parts of the South-west, and from Florida, where its place is taken by the Water-rat. It is a large rodent measuring up to two feet, of which ten inches is composed of a scaly, sparsely-haired tail that is compressed from side to side into a tapering scull. It is bulky and compact with broad feet, the hind pair of which are partially webbed. The waterproof coat consists of a thick, soft underfur, and a covering of long, shiny overhairs. In color it is various shades of rich brown above, darker on the mid-back, lighter and often reddish

123

Muskrat

on the flanks, and lighter below almost to white on the throat in some races. They are essentially aquatic animals, and are never found far from water. They also infest coastal marshes. They construct large winter "lodges" of cut vegetation which are sometimes built in holes under-ground but always above water level. They give off a rather pleasant, musky aromatic odor from special glands —hence their popular name. Up to a dozen rats may inhabit a single "lodge" or bank den, but they also con-struct individual feeding lodges. Several litters of up to nine young are produced in a season, after a 30-day ges-tation, and are weaned in less than a month.

5. NATIVE RATS AND MICE

More than half the species of rodents found in North America are contained in the great family known as the *Cricetidae*. This can be subdivided into, first, the Voles (*Microtinae*) and, secondly, the Native Rats and Mice (*Cricetinae*). The former are now regarded as being only a specialized form of the latter, but the division serves a useful purpose in breaking up this great host of little animals. The Cricetines are clearly divided, in turn, into Mice, Rats, and Woodrats.

A. NATIVE MICE

There are three distinct genera of Cricetines of small size and mouse-like form, which together inhabit almost the whole North American continent.

(1) White-footed Mice

The only mammals which may possibly approach the Field Voles (see page 114) in total population are the White-footed Mice (*Peromyscus: pera,* slender, *myscus,* mouse, Fig. 124). They are also found from the arctic tundras to the Florida swamps and the arid deserts, and up mountains to the limits of vegetation. There are a dozen species each represented by large numbers of regional races, but when live examples of any two species are viewed together their differences will be readily seen. They also vary considerably, some being arboreal and building nests in trees like those of squirrels, others living under logs or among rocks, and still others, especially on open prairies and deserts, living in underground burrows. In form they are typically mousy with slender bodies, rather long, pointed muzzles, large, delicate ears, neat little feet, and long tails, almost as long as the combined head and body. They average about seven to eight inches, of which three to four inches is tail. In color they vary above from very dark brown to reddish tinged with yellow, light brown tinged with yellow, light brown, or almost sandy in desert areas. There is invariably a light fluff at the base of the ears, and the eyes are enclosed in a darker area. The ears are naked and dark gray, the tail gray-brown above and white below. The whole underside including the feet, throat, cheeks and lower part of the muzzle is pure white. The base of the fur all over is dark slate gray. These mice take a mixed diet of seeds, berries, bulbs, insects, centipedes, caterpillars, and even small birds and other mice, but although they may consume quantities of stored grain, they are not so destructive to growing crops as the voles. They have a long breeding season and may produce several litters of from two to seven throughout the year in the South. The young are

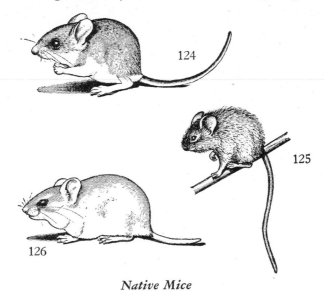

Native Mice

born in a compact, warm nest of all manner of soft materials and are weaned in three weeks and themselves ready to breed a month later. They progress by leaps rather than by running like the voles, and leave distinctive fairy tracks in mud or on snow, for they do not hibernate and are active throughout even the northern winter, though they then retire into concealed places and feed on large stores of food laid down during the fall. Sometimes several mice live together in burrows or nests, and they are adept at roofing over and reconstructing old birds' nests for their own use.

(2) Harvest Mice

These small mice (Fig. 125) measuring only five inches, of which two to two and a half inches is slender, slightly furred tail, may be distinguished from other species, and notably the introduced House Mouse which they greatly resemble, only by examining the front teeth. These are grooved, hence their name, *Reithrodontomys* (the mice with *rheithro*, grooved, teeth). They are southern forms ranging from Central America north throughout the southern states to Oregon, North Dakota, Wisconsin, southern Ohio, and Maryland in the east. They live in meadows and swamps and make small compact permanent nests with a single entrance raised from the ground or water among the grass stems, in which they live all year and raise their numerous small families. They are colored a plain dark brown above, and this color merges gradually into the grayish-brown underside. The feet are lighter gray.

(3) Grasshopper Mice

West of the Mississippi north to Alberta and west to the Pacific coast in California, and south to Mexico may be found representatives of two species of rather large, heavy-bodied, short-tailed mice known as *Onychomys* (or the clawed, *onychis*, mice, Fig. 126). They have soft, silky fur of various dull brown colors above, slightly darker along the middle of the back, and are pure white below, the two colors meeting along an abrupt line. The tail is less than a quarter the total length. They are completely nocturnal and live in burrows on the open plains, prairies, and deserts. They have moderate numbers of litters per year of only a few young each, and the parents go to exceptional pains, for rodents, in caring for them in a rather deep chamber amid a maze of tunnels. There are two distinct species having partly overlapping ranges in many places; one is distinctly the larger. The other has a somewhat longer tail, lives in the drier areas, and ranges in color from rather bright reddish-brown to a pale sandy tone above, often with a curiously pink tinge. Tufts of white hairs in the ears are noticeable. Their principal food is insects, and they are more generally carnivorous than any of our other rodents, even killing other mice.

B. NATIVE RATS

There are two species of Cricetines of a size warranting the term "rat." Both are southern forms.

(1) Rice Rats

On the lowlands of the southeast coast from New Jersey to Florida and thence west to the eastern coast of Texas, and north up the Mississippi Valley to Kentucky, Missouri, and Kansas, may be found a typical rat, with rather long, hard fur, an almost naked tail, very small, hairy ears, and small whiskers. These are known to farmers as Rice Rats, and to scientists as *Oryzomys* (from the Latin *oryza*, rice). They inhabit all types of treeless grassfields,

127

Rice Rat

swamps, meadows, and brush-covered localities. They are not unlike small Brown Rats (see p. 160) being various shades of gray-brown, or brown-gray above, and somewhat lighter below. The feet are light, sometimes almost white, and the tail is gray-brown and lighter below. There is usually some yellowish "wash" on the cheeks, side of neck, and often on the chest. They take to water readily and make nests above it in vegetation for choice, but they also burrow into banks and may be found even in fairly dense woodlands. They are prolific breeders, producing all year a series of litters numbering from two to seven young. The young are weaned rapidly and are very active from an early age. They appear to be retiring creatures and are seldom seen, since they are nocturnal. They have become a serious pest in some areas.

(2) Cotton Rats

These moderate-sized rats (*Sigmodon,* from the Greek letter, Σ, sigma, referring to the form of their cheek teeth) have comparatively short tails—somewhat less than half their total length. Despite the enormous numbers of other rodents, they hold a predominant position in the areas where they occur, which in North America cover the southern states from North Carolina via Tennessee, Arkansas, and northern Texas to Arizona. They are heavy-bodied rats, some ten inches long with short heads, large eyes and pronouncedly coarse, rough fur. They are a brindled blackish-brown with light flecks; the undersides

128

Cotton Rat

are light gray with a yellowish wash. They are inhabitants of grassfields and areas of vegetation, other than woods and forests, wherein they make endless runways and small nests. Their numbers are phenomenal, surpassing that of all other mammals put together in the areas where the environment suits their tastes. Moreover, they are more prolific than any of our other mammals, breeding either from winter to the following November, or throughout the year, having up to nine young at a litter; the young, it is said, are able to leave the nest and care for themselves in a week. Their principal food is grass, but they also eat insects and any animal food they can reach including eggs, fledgling birds, and even crabs, crayfish, and other aquatic animals.

C. WOODRATS

Although the average person revolts at the very name "rat," the animals we call Packrats or Woodrats, (*Neotoma*, the "fresh-cutter," referring to their habit of cutting and collecting sticks and other material) have nevertheless through their engaging habits insinuated themselves into the affections of many who have met them. There are about a dozen distinct species of *Neotoma* inhabiting North America, but the correct status of these forms is most unsatisfactory and requires new classification. Actually there are five distinct types distributed as follows: (1) a large southeastern race (Fig. 130), found in Florida and along the Gulf coast to central Texas and thence north to a line drawn from South Dakota to South Carolina, and west to Colorado. They have a rather short tail covered with a few short hairs, long fluffy fur which is pale gray-brown above washed with pinkish, and have creamy-white feet and undersides. They live in a variety of habitats but prefer woods or thick vegetation. They build large nests often in bushes or low trees; (2) a northeastern race found throughout the Appalachians from Tennessee to Connecticut, and west on to the lowlands of Kentucky, Ohio, West Virginia, and Pennsylvania. This is a larger species with very large ears and immense black and white whiskers. Its fur is buff-gray above and white below, and the long tail is dark above and light below. Its favorite habitat is rocks and caves where it accumulates huge piles of rubbish in its den; it is popularly known as the Cave Rat; (3) south of a line drawn from Oregon to central Texas and extending into Mexico may be found a group of half a dozen species with short to moderately long tails covered with stubby bristles. These animals are variously-colored gray-brown above and light below, and have white feet. In desert regions they may be very pale buff; (4) a large species on the Pacific coast of California distinguished principally by internal anatomical characters, but having dusky muffs on its ankles; and (5) the beautiful Rock Rats (Fig. 129) which are found all over the far West from the Yukon to the Dakotas, New Mexico, and California. The last are quite distinct animals with bushy, squirrel-like tails, furred ears, and white

129

130

Woodrats

feet and underparts. The tails are dark above and light
below. The eyes are large, the whiskers immense, and the
pellage usually pale gray. Woodrats make delightful pets,
and since they are intelligent, curious, and spotlessly
clean, may become as fully domesticated as any cat. In
the wilds they have certain remarkable habits. Some species build tremendous nests of sticks in low trees in which
several families may live together. Others accumulate
great piles of sticks, often including fair-sized branches,
against tree boles or rocks under which dome-shaped
nests and many large burrows or cleared tunnels are con-
structed. Others again haul material into caves and rock
crevices. Most extraordinary of all, however, is their habit
of collecting all manner of odd objects, especially shiny
things like tin cans, spoons, buttons, watches, etc. These
are taken to their woodpiles, but sometimes these amazing animals will bring pebbles or other natural objects
to replace their pilfered treasures. My tame ones spent
half their time substituting our cutlery for the writing
equipment on my desk.

6. POCKET-GOPHERS

Throughout the entire West from central British Columbia, Alberta, and Saskatchewan to Central America, and from the Pacific coast to the western foothills of the Appalachians, on the lowlands of the Gulf coast across to Georgia and Florida, may be found representatives of some four dozen different species of this uniquely North American family of Rodents, the *Geomyidae*, or *geo*, earth, *mys*, mice. They are somewhat ridiculous-looking beasts about the size of a large rat (nine to twelve inches long, of which two and a half to three and a half inches is tail) with gross, rather flabby bodies, short limbs, but tremendously developed and powerful forelegs bearing large digging claws. The tail, which is often naked, has a skin that seems to be too big for it, so that it wrinkles

131

Pocket-Gopher

and may be slipped up and down. The head is huge and flattened, and the jaw is grotesquely underslung so that the huge front teeth, and especially the lower pair, are exposed. What is more, the upper front teeth are carried out on a prolongation of the snout, and the furred skin of the cheeks actually meets behind them. Thus the mouth is reduced to a small round hole that can be plugged by the tongue from within. Pocket-Gophers are not likely to be mistaken for any other animal in any case, but should there be any doubt, you have only to capture the beast—taking the utmost care in handling it because they are tremendously strong, grumpy to the point of ferociousness, and can inflict a really terrible bite—turn it on its back and look for a pair of capacious, fur-lined pockets opening on each side of the mouth and extending back under the skin to the shoulders. The numerous types vary greatly in color from almost black in cool, damp areas, to very pale sandy-yellow in the hot deserts, for they live everywhere where the soil can be excavated and food exists. In cooler climes the fur tends to be thick and woolly or even silky, but in hot places it is coarse, hard, and hairy. There are two genera in North America delighting in the names of *Geomys* and *Thomomys* (the *thomé*, heap-making, mice) both very much alike. The former occupies the eastern and the latter the western half of their combined range. Pocket-Gophers are subterranean beasts living the lives of moles, seldom if ever venturing outside their holes except to snatch vegetation immediately around their entrance. They burrow continually in search of food, and drive side tunnels at short intervals from their main operations through which they evict the excavated earth. Their method of digging is remarkable, for they use their great front teeth as we would an adze, then scoop back the dirt under their chins with their forepaws. When enough has been accumulated they climb over the pile, turn round in the hole and, placing their forepaws together facing forwards, push the load back as we would do with a bulldozer. They can run backwards as fast as they can forwards, and they use their tails as tactile organs to feel out their way. Their food is all manner of roots, tubers, and bulbs. They can be highly destructive to crops, for example, neatly felling lines of young fruit trees by simply cutting them off below ground. What they do not eat they cut up and round off by holding the pieces between their forefeet and revolving them against their chisel-like teeth as we would do in a lathe. Then they flip them into their pouches and carry them off to large underground storage places. Litters of four to eight young are produced several times a year under stumps or stones in deep nests which are surrounded by curious, circular, blind tunnels. Only breeding females occupy such chambers.

7. POCKET-MICE

The seventh of the nine families of indigenous North American rodents is known technically as the *Heteromyidae*, or "the other mice"—a decidedly ambiguous definition. It is a small family of only five genera all of which have their headquarters in Central, and northern South America. They are distinguished by having fur-lined cheek pouches with external openings at the sides of the mouth, very long tails, and hind legs developed for jumping.

A. NORTH AMERICAN POCKET-MICE

Representatives of four of the genera occur in North America but the fifth and most numerous genus, that of the Spiny Rats, is confined to the tropics.

(1) The Spiny Mouse

One small Central American form spreads over our southern border into Texas. It is known as *Liomys* (the *leios*, smooth, mouse, Fig. 132) and has sprinkled through its fur a high percentage of sharp but pliant, flattened, dark-tipped spines shaped like long, thin spearheads. They are nocturnal mice of large size with a tail somewhat longer than the four-and-a-half-inch head and body. They are gray above with a brownish mid-back, and pure white below; the two colors meet at an abrupt line along the flanks, but are separated by a light orange stripe. The feet and hind limbs are white, and the tail is slate-colored above, and white below, with a dark tip. They burrow extensively in dry, open places, store food below ground, and bear several litters per year at all seasons of up to six young.

(2) Typical Pocket-mice

These very delicate mice, only two to four inches long, with tails of equal length or longer (*Perognathus*, the *peron* or "pointed," *gnathos*, jawed, Fig. 133) are distributed throughout the West from British Columbia and the Dakotas to Mexico, east to Oklahoma and Texas, and west to the Pacific coast. There are some two dozen recognized species and all of them vary in a bewildering manner, but they may be readily distinguished from all

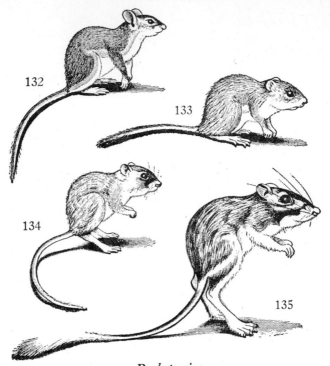

132

133

134

135

Pocket-mice

other North American rodents by their small size and externally opening cheek pouches. The fur may be very soft
and silky, coarse and hard, or either a mixture of hairs
and spines, or almost entirely spiny. The tail may be
naked, slightly haired, and bear a small crest of hairs or
a large terminal tuft, and may be evenly dark-colored,
dark above and light below, or particolored with a tuft.
The color ranges from black to buff. Most Pocket-mice
have white undersides and feet, and a distinct yellowish,
orange, or ochre line along the flanks between the upper
and underside colorations. They inhabit deserts and other
open dry places, are active only at night, and spend the
day in burrows which they plug up against the intrusion
of snakes and other predators. Although all their food is
dry seeds, they never drink even if water is available.

(3) Kangaroo Rats

These remarkable long-tailed rodents have been given the appropriate Latin name of *Dipodomys,* or the Two-footed Mice, Fig. 135, for they have long, stilt-like hind legs, and progress by hops and leaps, the small front limbs being held against the chest and never touching the ground while the animal is in motion. Kangaroo Rats are rather heavy-bodied, large-headed, small rats of various sizes from eight to fifteen inches in total length, more than half of which is accounted for by the great, tufted tail. This is a balancing organ and acts as a kind of rudder when the animal is in motion, aiding it in rapid turns by its counterbalancing weight, and probably also actually exerting some pressure against the air, for they travel at a remarkable speed. These rats have externally opening cheek pouches, large eyes, and very soft fur. The ears are small and round in shape, and the soles of the feet are clothed in thick, short, stiff fur. They are nocturnal and spend the day in burrows. They are found from northern California, Idaho, and Wyoming south to Mexico, and extend east to Oklahoma and central Texas. About two dozen species have been described, but they are all very much alike. They vary somewhat in colors but the arrangement of these is common to all. The top of the head, neck, and upper and outer sides of the body are dark, usually some shade of light reddish-brown, paling on the flanks and meeting the pure white underside at an abrupt line. The lower limbs are white. The face is white with dark cheeks and a dark band over the muzzle. There is a white stripe cutting straight across the thigh and round the rump above the tail. The tail itself is white above and below, and has a black stripe along either side, and a bushy black tip.

(4) Dwarf Kangaroo Rats

In limited, arid areas about the borders of Oregon, California, and Nevada live certain small, three-inch mice with long tails. They are known as *Microdipodomys,* Fig. 134, and resemble Pocket-mice but have smaller ears and longer hind legs. They are dark above and light below but washed with yellowish all over and especially on the flanks. They are nocturnal and live in burrows.

8. JUMPING-MICE

Throughout Canada and the United States, though never in great numbers, from the open arctic tundras south to about the 35th parallel north, may be found two very similar kinds of small mice without cheek-pouches, and with very long hind legs and tails. The head and body averages three and one-half inches, and the tail five and one-half inches in length. They are known as *Zapus* and *Napaeozapus,* or the *za,* sure, *pous,* footed, and *nape,* woodland, sure-footed ones respectively, and belong to a small family of ancient rodents of which the only other genus is a little striped mouse that lives in trees in parts of Eurasia. Species of *Zapus* are also found in China, but nowhere else outside North America. They are in no way

136

Jumping-Mouse

related to our Native Rats and Mice but stand somewhere between the Jerboas of the Old World and Porcupines. They are brownish-yellow above with a dark band down the mid-back, and pure white below. The ears are naked and rather small, the front limbs are short, and the hind legs very long, while the tail is extremely long and slender and usually dark above and light below; in *Napaeozapus* it has a white tip of sparse, long hairs. *Zapus* inhabits grasslands and mixed growth outside the woods and forests wherein *Napaeozapus* is found. They hibernate profoundly, living on an accumulation of fat, and build grass nests in fairly deep burrows. They eat insects as well as grains and wild berries. Two litters of up to half a dozen young are born in the summer months.

9. THE PORCUPINE

Nobody can mistake this large, stumpy-tailed rodent (*Erethizon,* the one who "rises in anger") , covered with very long hair interspersed with barbed spines that can be raised and shaken at will. There is a thick, soft underfur and the general color is black to very dark brown, sprinkled with various amounts of light, yellow-tipped, long, shiny, stiff hairs. The quills are light with black tips. They range in length from thirty to forty inches, of which only about six inches is tail. Porcupines are found throughout the forests of Canada and thence south in the east to Pennsylvania, and in the west via the Rockies almost to Mexico. They use their tails for defense, and since the barbed quills are only weakly joined to the skin, they

137

Porcupine

readily attach themselves to an enemy. Once so introduced, moreover, they are almost impossible for an animal to extract, and tend to work inwards, often eventually penetrating some vital organ. Porcupines can in no way "shoot" their quills. Their powers of gnawing are fantastic, and since they have a great predilection for salt, they will attack anything containing it and have actually gnawed through the bottoms of stout glass bottles. They are bumbling, crotchety beasts, but are extraordinarily capable and they fear nothing. They do not hibernate, are active in the severest weather, and bear only a single young, weighing a pound, which is relatively more than twelve times the weight of a human child at birth.

VII. AQUATIC MAMMALS

Under this perfectly legitimate heading are brought together the three remaining orders of mammals found in North America. It must, however, be clearly understood that although they all live either wholly in or exclusively by water, they are in no way related other than that they are all mammals. The seals are distant "cousins" of the *Carnivora*, the Manatee is a kind of aberrant ungulate showing some ancient relationship with the Elephants, Hyraxes, and Perissodactyles, and the Whales, while standing alone, seem to have had scaly terrestrial ancestors that probably sprang from the same stock as the Perissodactyles or odd-toed ungulates.

1. SEALS

This order, called that of the *Pinnipedia* (*pinna*, literally, a small kind of spatulate shell, *i.e.* the fin-shaped, *pedia*, footed ones) includes a number of flesh-eating animals with streamlined bodies, flipper-like fore limbs, and paddle-shaped hind limbs extending from the back end of the tapering body, all of which live in the sea. They are clothed in thick but usually short fur or hair, but in one case this is reduced to a few bristles on the muzzle.

A. EARED SEALS

The family *Otariidae* (or *otarion*, little-eared ones) is distinguished by having small external ears. They are the least specialized of seals with rather long necks, and they can turn their hind limbs forward, and thus "gallop" about on land to a limited extent.

(1) Sea Lions

From the Bering Straits to Mexico along the Pacific coast are found two distinct types of Sea Lions (Fig. 138). The northern (*Eumetopias*) meet the southern (*Zalophus, zale,* of the surf, the *ophion,* a fabulous sea beast,) in northern California. The males are much larger than the females, and those of the northern species may weigh over three quarters of a ton; those of the southern species weigh at most 650 lbs. They are clothed in short, coarse fur which shines when wet and is colored yellowish-brown above, somewhat lighter below when dry. Sea Lions have small claws on the second, third, and fourth toes of the hind feet, but a web extends beyond the digits. They are gregarious, congregating in colonies on the coast, and assembling in enormous numbers in May and June to breed at a few particular islands. The males arrive first. They have only one "pup" a year. Performing "seals" are invariably Sea Lions, and have much intelligence.

Eared Seals

(2) The Fur Seal

These animals (*Callorhinus,* the *calleo,* thick-skinned, *rhinos,* nosed ones) spend most of the year on the high seas of the north Pacific, but congregate once a year on the barren Pribiloff Islands in the Bering Sea to breed. They have a dense, yellowish underfur, but the coarse overfur renders the males black, and the females gray, above. Both are reddish-brown below. The males are slightly over six feet long and weigh up to 500 lbs.; the females are only about four feet long. Males develop an enormously swollen, domed forehead (see Fig. 139). One pup is born per year, but the males assemble harems of dozens of females. Demands of the fur trade reduced these seals to less than 150,000 by 1910, but there are now some 3,000,000 because of their careful protection.

B. EARLESS SEALS

The remaining seals have no external ear. Their necks are short, and the hind limbs are permanently directed backwards. There are claws on all the digits, and the soles of both fore and hind flippers are covered with fur. They constitute the family *Phocidae,* from the Latin, *phoca,* a seal.

(1) Common Seals

There are half a dozen seals of the genus *Phoca,* all of which are anatomically very much alike, but which display remarkable differences in coloration. All but one are small, averaging about five to six feet in length measured from nose to tail tip, the tail being about six inches long. The hind limbs extend beyond the tail and are about a foot in length. The commonest are the Harbor Seals of the North Atlantic and Pacific (Fig. 140), which are variously grayish-yellow with brown spots, or dark brown with yellow spots. The pups are almost white and are born in the spring. They stay by the coast, do not migrate or congregate to breed, and are found from the Arctic to Cape Hatteras in the Atlantic and to Mexico on the Pacific coast. A very large species known as the Greenland, Harp, or Saddle-backed Seal occurs in the North Atlantic. This can grow to eight feet in length and in old males may weigh as much as 800 lbs.; it is the basis of the maritime sealing industry. The adults are bright yellow with a dark brown mask and a circular band on the back (Fig. 141). They migrate annually to certain areas, notably off the mouth of the St. Lawrence, and the pure white, fluffy-furred pups are born on the floating ice floes where they are slaughtered for their pelts by clubbing in the most revolting of all human enterprises. All around the Arctic, but extending south only to Labrador in the Atlantic and the Aleutians in the Pacific, may be found the Ringed Seal (Fig. 142). It is similar to the Harbor Seal but colored dark brown with yellow, lozenge-shaped rings. The last and most remarkable member of the genus is the Ribbon Seal (Fig. 143) which is found off Alaska and the Aleutians. It is very dark brown with bright yellow rings around the neck, forelimbs, and tail.

140

141

142

143

144

145

146

EARLESS SEALS

(2) The Gray Seal

Known as the *Halichoerus* (*halo,* the sea, *choiros,* pig, Fig. 144), this is a large seal measuring up to twelve feet that is found only off the coasts of Greenland, Labrador, Newfoundland, and Nova Scotia. It is shiny, steel-gray in color, sometimes with vague darker dapplings on the upper sides and flanks. They inhabit rocky and inaccessible coasts, and delight in the heaviest ocean swells. Unlike other seals, they breed in the fall and do so singly at isolated points. They have an extraordinarily acute sense of smell.

(3) The Bearded Seal

This is one of the rarest of seals, *Erignathus,* (*erigo,* to raise, *gnathus,* the jaw, Fig. 145). It is of large size (up to twelve feet), and is found in the northern Atlantic, only from Newfoundland to the arctic ice, and in the Pacific off the coast of Alaska. It is somewhat variable in color but usually dark gray merging almost to black on the mid-back. It is solitary in habit and never congregates in either small or large parties. It spends much time on the ice floes and has a remarkable habit of turning a somersault when diving into the water. Its skin is exceptionally thick, and for this reason highly prized by the Eskimo for making lines and thongs. Its flesh is very tender. It bears a drooping moustache of large, flattened bristles; hence its popular name.

(4) The Crested Seal

Most remarkable of all our seals is the Crested Seal (*Cystophora cristata,* the crested, *kystis,* bladder, *phora,* bearing, one) which is common from the Arctic to Newfoundland. It migrates annually and breeds in small groups on the spring ice floes. It is an essentially open-ocean animal, and the sexes normally live apart. The outer toes of the hind flippers are much longer than the inner three, and long lobes of skin project beyond them. The color is bluish-black, lighter below, and dappled with white spots, especially on the flanks. The males have a curious bag of muscular tissue on the top of the fore-head that can be inflated from within at will (see Fig. 146). Males measure up to eight feet.

(5) The Sea-Elephant

This species (*Mirounga*) is the largest of all seals and is primarily an inhabitant of the Antarctic. There is, how-ever, an isolated colony in the northern hemisphere on islands off the coasts of California and Lower California. They were once numerous, and colonies occurred as far north as San Francisco, but they were all but extermi-nated by the end of the last century for their oil, of which a large male can yield over 200 gallons. They are now

147

Sea-Elephant

coming back under protection on Guadalupe Island, where there are over 500, and new colonies have recently appeared on the Coronados and Channel Islands off San Diego. The males reach eighteen feet in length, and may be as much as fifteen feet in girth; females are only about half that size. They are clothed in short, grayish-brown hair, but the pups are black. There are no claws on the hind feet and the males have a sixteen-inch, in-flatable trunk penetrated by the nostrils; this normally droops over the mouth but can be raised almost straight up. They molt once a year and then the skin as well as the hair comes off in large patches; the new skin is bright pink. Their food is cuttlefish, seaweed, and shellfish.

C. THE WALRUS

This enormous denizen of the arctic seas, now found only in very restricted areas off northern Greenland and in the Bering Straits, constitutes a separate family of the *Pinnipedia,* known as the *Odobaenidae,* or those who *baino,* walk with their, *odo,* teeth, because they sometimes use their tusks to obtain a purchase upon the ice when climbing out of the water. They are generally seal-like but are tailless and can turn the hind limbs forward to aid in humping along on ice or land. There are flat nails on all digits of the fore flippers, and on the outer

148

The Walrus

digits of the hind flippers. They are hairless, except for a profuse "Old Bill" moustache of curved, stiff bristles, and the skin is wrinkled, warty, and rough. They are of great bulk; large males measure up to twelve feet and weigh as much as a ton and a half. The females are only about two-thirds as big. The upper canine teeth are developed into huge, down-curving tusks projecting from the mouth to as much as eighteen inches. The sixteen remaining teeth are adapted for crushing the hard food which consists of starfish, shellfish, and other crustaceans. The one or two pups which are born in late spring are suckled for two years.

2. SEA COWS

Half a dozen species of Manatee found in the rivers and along the Atlantic coasts of tropical America and Africa, a related animal known as the Dugong found in Australia and the Oriental region, and a huge creature called Steller's Sea Cow that lived off Alaska but was exterminated only in the last century constitute the order called *Sirenia* or "sirens," because they have the habit of standing upright half out of water holding their young in one flipper while suckling them, and are thus thought to have been the inspiration of the Mermaid myth. Mermaids distracted sailors like the sirens of fable.

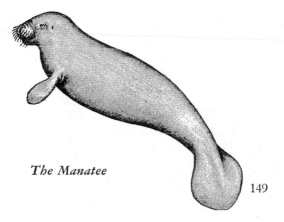

The Manatee

149

A. THE MANATEE

Found along the coasts of Florida and the Gulf in limited areas, the Manatee grows to twelve feet in length and may weigh a ton. It is seal-shaped but has lost the hind limbs, and instead has a large, paddle-shaped, horizontal tail. There is virtually no neck and the head is small and blunt, with bulbous upper lips divided down the middle, and nostrils with valves which can close. They are hairless and colored neutral gray, but have rather intelligent-looking light-brown eyes. They live in shallow seas, lagoons, estuaries, and rivers, and feed on submerged vegetation, but they reach out onto the banks to crop grass, and tame ones will take bread out of your hand. They have one young per year.

3. WHALES

The order *Cetacea* (from the Greek, *ketos,* a whale) includes just a hundred species of somewhat fish-shaped mammals that occur in all oceans, most seas, in the rivers of the tropics, and in certain freshwater lakes. They vary in size from the greatest of all animals, the Blue Whale, to a three-foot creature found in the upper tributaries of the Amazon, and include dolphins, porpoises, blackfish, the beluga, and the narwhal. They are descended from animals that lived on land, but are of extremely ancient origin, and there is some evidence to show that their ancestors bore bony plates in their skins, as do the armadillos, and that they first took to water along the banks of tropical rivers. They have lost their hind limbs and hip girdles which may be found in some species as a series of tiny bones loose in the flesh behind the stomach. They have streamlined, spindle-shaped bodies and horizontal tails with two flukes. The eyes are small and the ear openings minute. The skin is hairless and sometimes very thin, but a thick layer of fibrous fat or "blubber" underlies it. They give birth to a single calf in the water, and suckle it therein. They grow very rapidly. The nostrils open on the top of the head. *Cetacea* are clearly divided into two groups, the Baleen and the Toothed Whales.

A. BALEEN WHALES

There are only a dozen species of Baleen Whales, all marine, and all large. They have very large heads and enormous mouths, and in place of teeth the ridges across their palates have become horny (*i.e.* "whalebone") and developed into a double series of triangular plates edged with hair-like fringes. These depend from the roof of the mouth just inside the upper jaws, and increase in size from front and back to the center. Their fringed edges present an inverted dome of matting against which the huge tongue is pressed upwards to force out water taken in with the masses of small food. The food of the largest species is a small shrimp-like animal known as "krill," that of the smaller species is various fish ranging in size from sardines to herring. Baleen whales prefer cold water.

(1) Right Whales

The family *Balaenidae,* or Right Whales, are so-called because they were the *right* ones to harpoon in old whaling days, for they did not sink when dead. They have no upright, triangular fin in the middle of the back, and their mouths are enormous. There are two species. The Black Whales (Fig. 152) were once common throughout the North Atlantic and Pacific, but were almost exterminated by early whalers for their oil used for lighting, and their baleen which was used for stiffening ladies' corsets, making hair brushes, and, in early days, the plumes for knights' helmets. They are normally black all over, but one in five has a white belly. The baleen is up to seven feet long. On the tip of the snout is a large growth of irregular, horny material called the "bonnet" which is infested with barnacles, marine worms and other parasites. Black Rights migrate south in winter to the mid-North Atlantic and Pacific, and back to the Arctic in summer, where they gather in herds called "gams." There is a single calf nursed for a year. The Arctic Right Whale, also known as the Bowhead or Greenland Right Whale (Fig. 153), also occurs in the North Atlantic and Pacific but stays by the ice front all year. Like the Black Right Whale it grows to a length of 50 to 65 feet. The head is even more enormous and may have up to 300 plates of baleen, the longest measuring 12 feet. It also feeds on krill and other tiny creatures. It is velvety-black in color, with light lower jaw, cream-colored throat, and it sometimes has white areas all over. It has a few scattered white hairs on the tip of the snout and lower jaw. This species was not discovered until the sixteenth century, when the Basque whalers reached Greenland waters. They immediately recognized its value, and together with the Dutch, who were then entering the whaling business, they hunted it assiduously from Spitzbergen. Baleen at one time commanded the extraordinary price of $5.00 per pound, and since up to 3000 lbs. could come from a single whale, this treasure could cover the entire cost of fitting out the whaling vessel for a season. The same species was later hunted in the Bering Sea and the Sea of Okhotsk, where the animals appear to have bred.

(2) Rorquals

Rorquals (family *Balaenopteridae*) are distinguished by having an upright, triangular fin on the back, longer and slenderer form, and a series of longitudinal folds or pleats extending from the chin to the chest or belly. Five species occur off our coasts. The largest is the Blue Whale (Fig. 150) which reaches 115 feet in length and weighs up to 125 tons. It is blue-black above and white below, mottled with pale gray. It has up to 400 baleen plates, but these are only three feet long. A 25-foot, 8-ton, unborn baby was taken from an 80-foot female. The calves double their size in a year, and are mature in two years and breeding in three. Blue Whales eat krill, and migrate

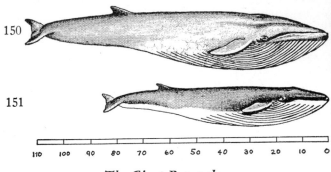

The Giant Rorquals

north and south after them. The commonest species of rorqual (Fig. 151) is also known as the Finback Whale or Finner, and has been the mainstay of the modern whaling industry since the invention of the harpoon gun by Sven Foyn, and the use of steam chasers, power winches, and, more recently, factory ships, radar, bombs, and electrocution devices. It is smaller and sleeker than the Blue Whale, growing up to 80 feet in length, and having 100 pleats on the throat. The color is slate gray above, and white below. It is a very fast swimmer, and goes about in schools of up to 300. It eats krill and fish, and has a single calf which is suckled for six months. The vapor from the blowhole spouts 20 feet into the air. The right side of the head is always lighter in color than the left.

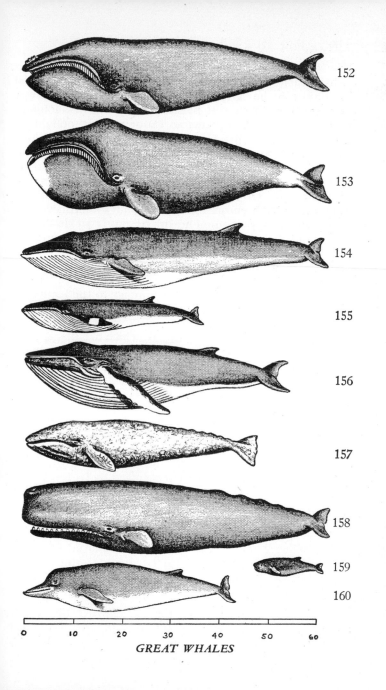

152

153

154

155

156

157

158

159

160

0   10   20   30   40   50   60

GREAT WHALES

The third species is the Sei Whale, so-called because it arrives each year on the north Norwegian coast at the same time as the "seje" or Black Cod. This rorqual (Fig. 154) was once thought to be either the young of the finner or very rare. It only grows to about 55 feet, and has a sharp-pointed snout; the blow-holes lie in two longitudinal furrows. The "spout" is about 14 feet high and drifts off in vapor. Seis are great wanderers, following the "krill" and even smaller pelagic crustaceans from the ice front to the tropics where they breed. They are bluish-gray above, lighter on the flanks, and sometimes have small, silver-gray spots. The dorsal fin is sickle-shaped and about two-thirds back along the body. They have from 40 to 60 pleats on the throat. The Little Piked Whale is also known as the "Seigval" or Codfish Whale (Fig. 155). It feeds on fish, and never exceeds 35 feet in length. It also migrates north in summer to the ice front, and likes to associate with the larger rorquals. It is dark blue-black above, and white below except for the two outer of the 60 pleats on the throat, which are black. The flippers are white below and black above, with a prominent white stripe across their upper half. The word "piked" is Scotch for the tall, pointed back fin. The last species of rorqual is the Humpback (Fig. 156) which was once a very common and widespread species preferring the proximity of coasts and living alone or in small parties, but sometimes congregating in large schools. It has been mercilessly persecuted by whalers but is still fairly prevalent in both the Atlantic and Pacific. It grows to a length of 50 feet, and is easily recognized by its long, narrow flippers with nodules all along their front edges. The lower jaw projects beyond the upper and there are only about 30 pleats on the throat. The hind edge of the tail is slotted. They are black above and mottled with dirty white below. There is a small dorsal fin placed far back on the body. They are playful creatures at the best of times, but in the mating season the pairs deliver "love-pats" with their flippers that may be heard for miles. They eat krill and some small fish, and migrate annually to and from the cold polar waters.

The rorquals are the most prevalent whales in the seas today, and enormous numbers of them are killed annually by the whalers of the modern industry, almost all in the Antarctic. After World War II, an international agreement was reached whereby 16,000 units are allowed to be taken per season; a unit is based on the Blue Whale, equal to which are either two Finners, two and a half Humpbacks, or six Sei Whales. In 1946-47, 21,729 whales were taken, composed of 8,870 Blues, 12,857 Finners, and 2 Sei, a number that surpasses several years' catch by the total New England whaling fleet in the heyday of the so-called Golden Age of whaling. Yet, the larger whales are no longer in danger of total extermination, for contrary to previous opinion, it has now been discovered that these great mammals are fairly prolific and reach maturity very rapidly. The value of an 89-foot female Blue Whale weighing 150 tons was $27,000 when fully processed, in 1950.

(3) The Gray Whale

The Gray Whale (Fig. 157) is the most primitive of the Baleen Whales; it constitutes a separate family, *Rhachianectidae,* which was once common throughout the north Pacific. Two skeletons of this species were also found by the Dutch when they drained part of the Zuider Zee, showing that it once had a much wider distribution. It lives by the coast and feeds in the seaweed beds in shallow water. A whole industry was founded upon its capture on our west coast in the last century, as it migrated bi-annually up and down from the Arctic to the tropics. This came to an end when the whales were exterminated, and the species was thought to be extinct until Roy Chapman Andrews rediscovered it in Korea. It grows to a length of 50 feet, has a small head, only four pleats on the throat, and few, very heavy and thick baleen plates about 18 inches long. It is slate-gray in color, but the body is normally covered with white scars formed where masses of whale lice or barnacles have grown. The females are larger than the males. They have irregular rows of stiff hairs all over the top and sides of their heads. They have now reappeared on the California coast, and may still make a comeback. They can swim in very shallow water and will attack small boats if molested.

B. TOOTHED WHALES

All the remaining whales are grouped together and appear to have had a common origin. There are six families, five of them represented by species that inhabit our coasts. The only one absent is that of the River Dolphins (*Platanistidae*) that are confined to tropical freshwaters.

(1) Sperm Whales

There are only two members of the family *Physeteridae,* the great Cachalot or Sperm Whale, and the Pygmy Sperm, both distinguished by having teeth in the lower jaw only, and an organ in the forehead that contains a light, viscous wax known as *spermaceti*. The Sperm Whale (*Physeter catodon*, Fig. 158) is probably the best known of all whales, since it was the foundation of the New England industry and so gave us oil for our lamps before the discovery of petroleum; it was also the villain of "Moby Dick." It is a vast beast, the males of which once grew to 85 feet in length, but which now seldom exceed 60 feet, with a large "tank" on the front of its head that gives the muzzle a square profile. The head is almost a third the total length, and the skull inside is completely lopsided. There is a single S-shaped blowhole on the left side of the snout. Instead of a dorsal fin there are a descending series of bumps on the after back; the flippers are broad and small, and the lower jaw is long and narrow, and armed with up to 30 teeth on each side. These fit into holes in the toothless upper jaw. They feed on squids, crustaceans, and some fish, for which they dive to enormous depths, staying down for 20 minutes to an hour and a quarter. One became entangled in an ocean cable at a depth of 5000 feet, and was drowned. Its body was hauled up with the cable. The Pygmy Sperm Whale (Fig. 159) is only 13 feet long, has never been seen alive on the high seas, but has occasionally been washed up on our shores. It is black above, light gray below, and has a narrow pink mouth with 15 sharp, recurved teeth on each side of the lower jaw. The head is blunt and rounded, and contains a small tank of spermaceti. It also feeds on squids.

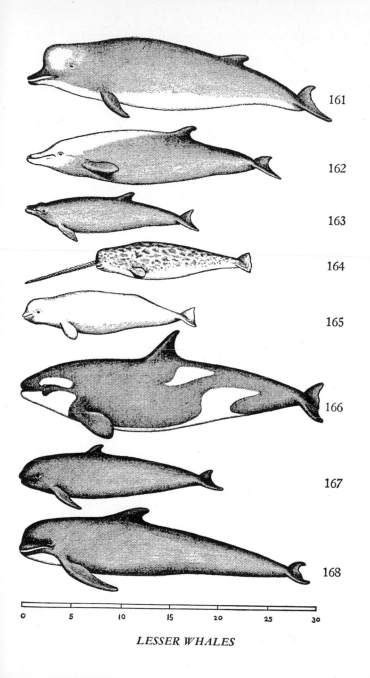

161

162

163

164

165

166

167

168

LESSER WHALES

(2) Beaked Whales

There are four genera of medium to small whales which, though inhabiting the open oceans, are sometimes washed up on our shores. These are known as the Beaked Whales (*Ziphiidae,* from *xiphos,* a sword). One, the Bottlenosed Whale (Fig. 161), once supported a special industry, since it is fairly common and carries a high-grade oil in its bulbous forehead. Males grow to 30 feet, females to 25 feet. They are gray-brown above, lighter below and have light-yellowish heads. There are a pair of teeth buried in the front end of the lower jaw. Baird's Whale (Fig. 160) which grows to 40 feet, is found in the Pacific. It is gray above and white below and has a long beak and two pairs of teeth at the front end of the lower jaw. Cuvier's Whale (Fig. 162) only reaches 20 feet in length, is found in both the Atlantic and Pacific, and has a large pair of teeth at the extreme front end of the lower jaw. It is also dark gray above and lighter below, often with a white head and neck. No less than five species of the last genus (*Mesoplodon,* Fig. 163) have now been recorded from our shores. These are the Strap-Toothed Whales, all about 20 feet long when full grown, with pronounced beaks and a single pair of flattened, incurved teeth placed about half-way along the lower jaw.

(3) White Whales

This family, the *Monodontidae* (or one-toothed ones) contains two of the most remarkable of all mammals. They are of small size, males reaching only 12 feet, are without dorsal fins, have small tails, and flippers placed far forward under their small heads. They are both arctic animals inhabiting the North Atlantic. The Narwhal (*Monodon monoceros,* the single-toothed, single-horned one, Fig. 164), is blotched and dappled with light and dark gray or yellow, but is almost pure white when old. Males have one or sometimes two immense spears, having invariably a left-hand twist, protruding from the front of their heads. These are the canine teeth, which in the females are buried in the skull. The Beluga (*Delphinapterus*), Fig. 165, is pure white, has no horn, but is prized for the fine leather which is made from its hide. It occurs in the St. Lawrence estuary.

(4) Porpoises

We have two true porpoises (*Phocaenidae*) on the coasts of North America, the Common or Harbor species (Fig. 172) which is dark gray above, only a little lighter below, and has a blunt, beakless head and a small, triangular dorsal fin, and Dall's Porpoise of the north Pacific coasts. This is black above and white below. Both grow to a length of six feet and the Common species is found on both coasts but not in the Arctic. They go about in small schools and ascend rivers. They feed on fish. Porpoises have spade-shaped crowns on their teeth quite unlike those of any other whales. They also have complex stomachs with a "crop."

(5) Dolphins

All the remaining whales found around North America are members of the Dolphin family (*Delphinidae*) but they vary enormously in size, shape, color, and habits. The Killer Whales (Fig. 166) are the largest and most terrible flesh-eating animals that we know of on our planet. Males, which are almost twice the size of the females, have been recorded up to 30 feet in length, and they are always of great girth. They have a dozen huge, sharp, even, recurved teeth on each side of each jaw, and will attack anything in the sea. They travel in packs of up to 40 together, and male walrus, the largest sharks, and all other whales flee from them. They will rip out the tongues of the Right Whales, have been seen to tear a Gray Whale to pieces, and one was caught choking to death on the fifteenth seal it was trying to swallow. They have attacked men by charging up from under the ice, and by smashing small white boats, possibly under the impression that these were whales. Our figure shows the common species; there is another in the Pacific that lacks the white spot behind the eye. The dorsal fin may reach six feet in length and turn over at the tip. The False Killer (Fig. 167), although of almost equally terrifying appearance, being barrel-shaped, and with a mouthful of large, blunt teeth, seems, however, to be a fish eater of mild disposition. They are dark gray all over, have a small dorsal fin and narrow, pointed flippers. They

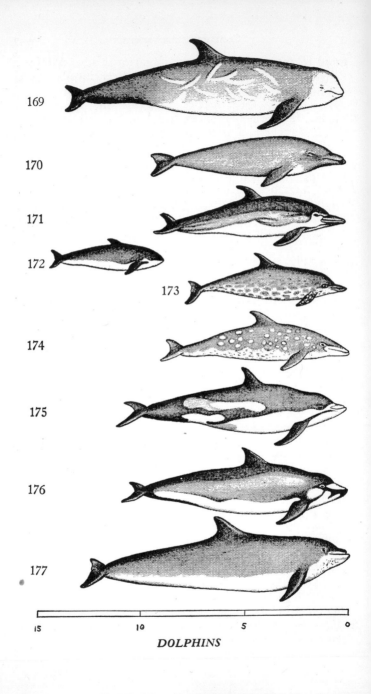

169

170

171

172

173

174

175

176

177

15   10   5   0

DOLPHINS

grow to fifteen feet and are gregarious. The Blackfish, Pilot Whale, or Caa'ing, is termed scientifically *Globicephalus,* or "the Roundhead," which aptly describes it (Fig. 168). Several species occur in the Atlantic and Pacific, the former often having a narrow white area on the lower chest. The flippers are long and slender, the dorsal fin is sickle-shaped. They are called Pilot Whales because they travel in schools following a leader, and if he runs aground, they all follow him blindly ashore. They have been systematically herded thus in the Faröe Islands since early Norse times, and they are stranded on our coasts almost yearly, much to the amazement of the public. The name Grampus is often misleadingly applied to the Killer, but it properly belongs to a small whale (Fig. 169) growing to a length of 13 feet, and of odd color. Basically it is grayish-yellow above with almost yellow face, black fins and tail, and white below, and it is covered with light streaks and spots probably caused by the suckers of octopus and squids on which it feeds. It has only a few teeth at the front of the mouth. The Right Whale Dolphins are curious, jet-black, eight-foot whales without dorsal fins, and shaped not unlike tiny Right Whales (Fig. 170). The lower jaw protrudes beyond the upper, and some have a white band across the chest. There are also no less than five genera of typical dolphins found round our coasts, the forms of which may be seen from the accompanying illustrations. The Common Dolphin (*Delphinus,* Fig. 171) is bluish-black above and silvery below, with varicolored streaks on the flanks. It has a pronounced beak and numerous sharp teeth. The Spotted Dolphin (*Prodelphinus,* Fig. 173) is seven feet long, dark above, light below with lines of dark spots. The Long-beaked Dolphin (*Steno,* Fig. 174) is pronouncedly black and white. The White-sided and White-beaked Dolphins, Figs. 175 and 176 respectively, belong to the same genus (*Lagenorhynchus*) and are gregarious northern forms. The former often have bright yellow side-streaks. The Bottlenosed Dolphins (*Tursiops,* Fig. 177) are the basis of a fishery off Cape Hatteras. Dolphins are the swiftest things in the sea apart from some of the squids which they pursue and some have kept pace with the Queen Elizabeth for hours.

VIII. THE NEWCOMERS

There is one mammal which we have so far neglected but which has played a larger part in the biological life of our planet since the last retreat of the ice caps and which has probably altered the natural balance and economy of the world more than any other in geological history. This mammal is Man. Moreover, his influence is twofold. First, he is himself a fairly large animal—the average size of all living things is a housefly; of mammals, the Wolverine (see p. 62) —and man has now increased in numbers to some two and a quarter billions. Thus, humanity represents some 145 million tons of living flesh that has to be fed at least twice a day to keep healthy, and this puts a considerable strain on the other animals and on plants. Since it takes several acres to feed a family, man has already partially swamped the earth. Secondly, man has domesticated many species of animals, and has moved them all over the earth with him. Sometimes these have run away, gone wild, and established themselves in new countries, ousting indigenous wild species, and otherwise upsetting the balance of Nature. The change in North America wrought by the introduced European and African races of man is obvious to everybody; the effects produced by his domestic and runaway or "feral" animals is not so obvious and is often overlooked. There are over 230,000,000 domestic, and unknown millions of feral, mammals in North America. Their effect upon nature is very marked.

1. FLESH-EATING MAMMALS

The Amerindians domesticated certain wild dogs or brought them from Asia at an early age. Domestic cats were, however, unknown.

A. CATS

This ubiquitous companion of man (see p. 37) is known to have been among the passengers aboard the Mayflower, and it has been constantly reintroduced ever since. The present cat population of the United States is calculated to be twenty-one millions, of which no less than ten and a half million are strays. In some areas, and notably the forests of Florida, Pennsylvania, and Virginia, stray or abandoned cats have gone completely feral, and by free breeding have in some cases produced an animal of almost double normal size with coloration not unlike the original wild cats of Africa, and even, on occasion, with small ear-tufts like a Bobcat. In other areas they have developed a pure black strain. Feral cats have crossbred with Bobcats in Florida and Texas. Those in Florida have not yet produced live young, but in Texas they have done so. Feral cats once became so numerous in Virginia that they were pronounced legal game.

178

Coyote-dog

B. DOGS

Though no proper census of the domestic dog population of North America has ever been taken, it is estimated by the most likely sources to know that there is at least one dog per ten persons, or some seventeen million in the United States and Canada. However, though dogs appear to find it harder to subsist in the wild without human aid, at least in temperate climes, feral dogs still sometimes become quite a problem, notably in Virginia, and recently in New Jersey within 30 miles from New York. There are some small packs which regularly hunt deer in the Adirondacks, and these have lately been reported as interbreeding with the Coyote (page 45) to produce the rather grim-looking animal shown above, which has caused some concern, but mostly in the press.

2. HOOFED MAMMALS

Our indigenous hoofed mammals, exclusive of the forest deer (see p. 80), have suffered from the advent of the white man much more severely than any of the other groups of mammals. The great Bison herds are gone, the Mountain Sheep, Goats, Pronghorn, and Reindeer have been greatly restricted and reduced in numbers, the Wapiti and Moose have vanished from more than half their original range. Now, Nature abhors a vacuum of any kind, be it complete or partial, and seems almost to aid in the refilling of any natural niche which becomes empty. Thus the grasslands have been a constant temptation to the grazing animals introduced by man. All of them have at one time or another managed to escape to at least temporary freedom. These semi-wild animals, together with the vast domesticated herds listed below, have very materially affected not only the wild life but even the vegetative cover of large parts of the continent, and in a few cases have virtually eliminated the entire vegetation.

A. CATTLE

In 1949 there were seventy-eight million domestic cattle in the United States alone. Many of these roam areas in the West in conditions very like those which they would encounter in the wild state. They thus affect the wild life and vegetation as would herds of big game. However, in certain areas cattle have carved out unusual habitats for themselves, as in the coastal swamps of the South. There are a few herds—notably preserved on the Wichita Wildlife Refuge near Cache, Oklahoma—of the American Longhorn which is descended from a breed brought by the Spanish, and *not* from the English Longhorn. Under ideal natural conditions they have developed into the most magnificent beasts, usually black or white, with enormous horns. European breeds of cattle have shown a tendency to deteriorate rather rapidly when turned completely loose on the "ranges" of the West. Zebu, the Humped Cattle of south Asia, were also introduced to strengthen the strain and in the hope of developing breeds immune to cattle fever.

B. SHEEP

Sheep were once much more numerous in the United States than they are today. In 1920 there were over sixty million, but by 1949 their number had dropped to thirty-eight million. Moreover, the great sheep-raising area was originally New England, but has now moved to the West. Sheep produce their most pronounced effect on the natural economy by maintaining pastures, or rather by holding back other growth that might invade grasslands. Their overall effect is beneficial. They do best on upland, dry areas in temperate climes. The famous lop-eared Navajo Sheep of the West constitute a distinct and unique American breed.

C. GOATS

These animals are not as popular in North America as in most other continents, but there are still four and a half million here on ranches or farms, or living in a feral condition. The goat is a very worthy animal when kept in control, but one of the most dangerous when let loose, because it breeds fast and can literally eat up the whole country. Goats can live on vegetation so scanty that it will not support any other animals, and they can even sip sea-water if fresh water is not available. The ultimate results of this may be seen on certain islands off our coast where these animals have completely eliminated the natural flora and, with it, the fauna.

D. PIGS

Introduced both from Europe and China, the domestic pig early learned that the forests of the South lacked an indigenous animal of their size and proclivities, and large numbers immediately adopted a feral life. The southern witticism to the effect that there are twice as many hog-owners as hogs in the backwoods is often true because nobody actually owns any of them. Moreover, as these pigs are highly prolific, have no natural enemies, and eat almost anything, including even a snake if necessary, they have very materially altered the faunal balance in some areas. There are also sixty-two million pigs in proper domestication in North America.

E. HORSES

Although the number of horses has naturally been greatly reduced because of their progressive replacement by the gasoline engine, there are still eleven million of them in the United States and Canada. The horse is essentially an animal of the open plains, and at various times very large herds have run wild in the West. North America was populated with truly wild horses up till comparatively recent geological times, but they had become totally extinct, probably due to some disease, thousands of years before the coming of the white man. Strange, small, feral races have been developed, notably on Chincoteague Island off the coast of Virginia, but the exaggerated abnormalities with long body and only half the normal length of leg, often exhibited alive, and reported to come from an isolated, waterless sink-hole near the Grand Canyon, have been proved to be artificially created on a ranch in Mexico. They are only Shetland Pony runts whose growth has been somehow stopped. The normal wild Fuzz-tail Horse of the Southwest stands only about four feet at the shoulder, and weighs only 300 lbs., which is certainly small enough.

F. DONKEYS

Donkeys were originally desert animals, and they do best in hot, arid regions. However, the great demand for mules which continues—for there are still some three and a half million in the United States—obviously cannot be maintained without donkeys, because mules are merely a sterile cross between horses and donkeys. The patient little burro, however, does not play a prominent part in either our own or the natural economy of the continent, though it is the mainstay of peasant Mexico.

G. CAMELS

A curious experiment was once tried in Texas. Camels were imported from Africa for army patrol duty against Indian marauders prior to the Civil War. They were not a success, and a number were turned loose. As far as is known they did not breed, and died off. However, lone hunters constantly report seeing them, although no case has ever been authenticated.

3. MAMMALS THAT GNAW

Several Rodents have been introduced into North America both wittingly and unwittingly. There can hardly be a more dangerous procedure, except perhaps the uncontrolled introduction of insects, for rodents can become terrible pests—*vide* rabbits in Australia, and the Muskrat in Europe. The most disastrous additions to the North American fauna were undoubtedly the Black and Brown Rats. There are now more of these than people in the United States, and not only do they spread disease but they also eat two hundred million bushels of our grain per year, and altogether cause over two billion dollars worth of damage.

179

The Nutria

A. THE NUTRIA

An example of a successful and beneficial introduction of a foreign animal is that of the South American aquatic rodent, the Nutria or Coypu (*Myopotamus*). These were first imported in 1899. Farming was begun in earnest in the 1920's but failed, and the big Muskrat-like mammals were released. Surprisingly, they found for themselves a perfect natural niche that was apparently not filled by any wild animal, and were soon well-established in Louisiana, Mississippi, Texas, and Washington. They are ten times the size of Muskrats, and their pelts are worth $3.50 each. During the next decade their furs are expected to surpass those of Muskrat in volume and value. They live amicably with Muskrats and eat food the latter spurn.

B. RATS

There are two species of rats that have colonized the whole earth, along with European man. The Black Rat (*Rattus rattus*, Fig. 180) was originally an Oriental Tree-Rat, and is still a climber; the Brown Rat (*Rattus norvegicus*, Fig. 181) is indigenous to the open grassy steppes of central Asia, and is a digger of holes. Fleas parasitizing the former carry bubonic plague; the latter infest sewers and contaminate stored food. They are our greatest com-

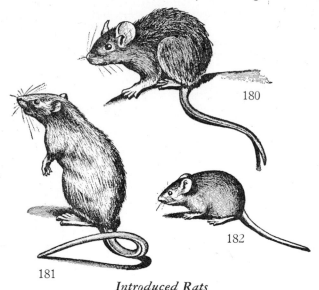

Introduced Rats

petitors for life. Rats are highly adaptable and have a definite social system; they can cooperate among themselves, and are highly ingenious and prolific.

C. THE HOUSE MOUSE

This tiny, competent rodent (*Mus musculus*, Fig. 182) has also followed European man everywhere, even to the Antarctic, and it has been grossly maligned. It does destroy some of our stores and create a mess, but on the whole it does good by keeping down cockroaches and other insect pests. Mice are rather beautiful, delicate little creatures, and can easily be tamed.

INDEX

It is assumed that zoologists, naturalists, and other specialists who work by the Latin nomenclature will be sufficiently familiar with the classification of the mammals to find whatever genus or species they wish without using this index of popular names.

Regional popular names which are outright misnomers—*i.e.*, long-established and internationally recognized as applying to other animals not found in North America—are shown in italics.

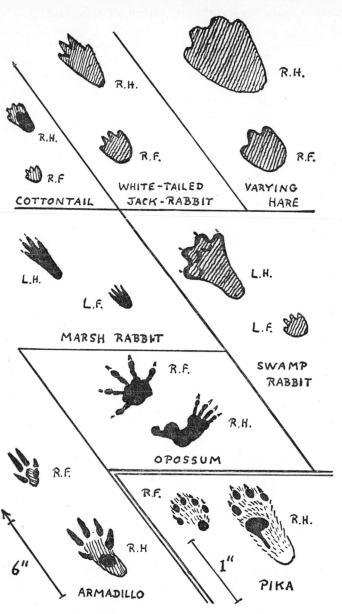

R.H.

R.H.

R.H.

R.F.

R.H.

R.F.

R.F.

COTTONTAIL

WHITE-TAILED
JACK-RABBIT

VARYING
HARE

L.H.

L.H.

L.F.

L.F.

MARSH RABBIT

R.F.

SWAMP
RABBIT

R.H.

R.F.

OPOSSUM

R.F.

R.F.

R.H.

6"

1"

ARMADILLO

R.H

PIKA

Hares, Rabbits, and Ancient Ones

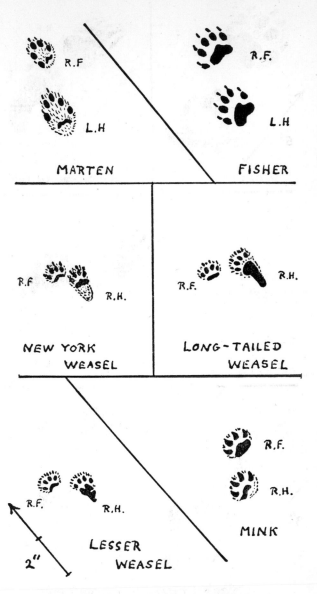

R.F

L.H

MARTEN

R.F.

L.H

FISHER

R.F.

R.H.

NEW YORK
WEASEL

R.F.

R.H.

LONG-TAILED
WEASEL

R.F.

R.H.

LESSER
WEASEL

2"

R.F.

R.H.

MINK

The Weasel Family—Small Ones

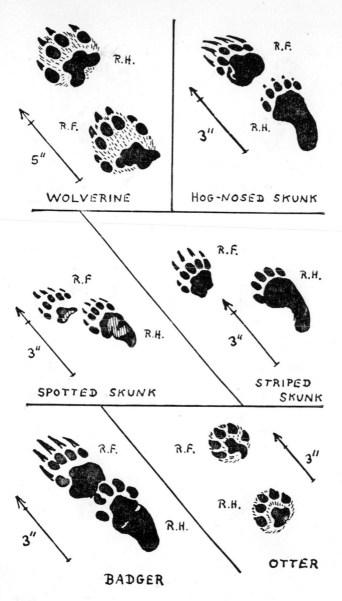

WOLVERINE

R.H.

R.F.

5"

HOG-NOSED SKUNK

R.F.

R.H.

3"

SPOTTED SKUNK

R.F

R.H.

3"

STRIPED SKUNK

R.F.

R.H.

3"

BADGER

R.F.

R.H.

3"

OTTER

R.F.

R.H.

3"

The Weasel Family—Large Ones

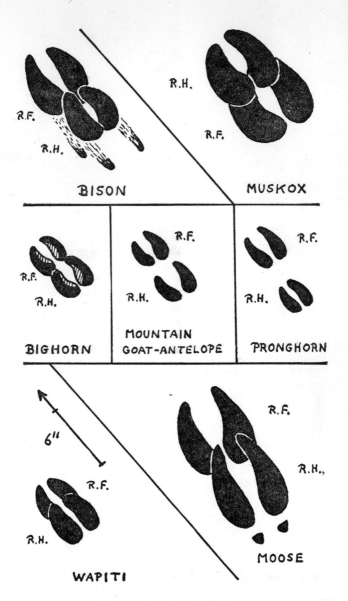

BISON

MUSKOX

BIGHORN

MOUNTAIN
GOAT-ANTELOPE

PRONGHORN

WAPITI

MOOSE

Greater Hoofed Ones

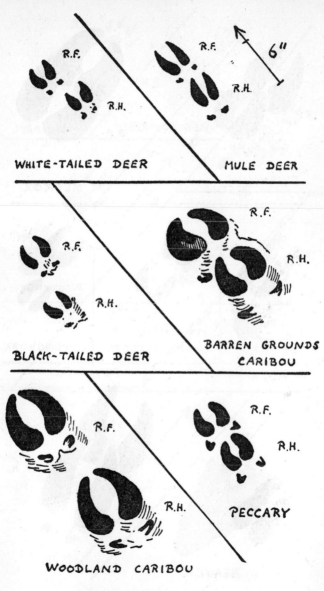

R.F.

R.F.

6"

R.H.

R.H.

WHITE-TAILED DEER

MULE DEER

R.F.

R.F.

R.H.

R.H.

BLACK-TAILED DEER

BARREN GROUNDS
CARIBOU

R.F.

R.F.

R.H.

R.H.

PECCARY

WOODLAND CARIBOU

Lesser Hoofed Ones

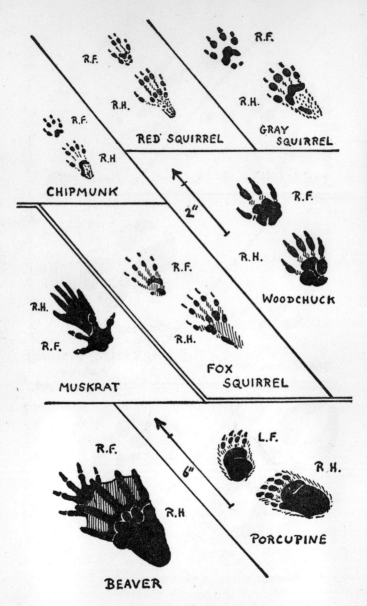

R.F.

R.F.

R.F.

R.H.

CHIPMUNK

RED SQUIRREL

R.F.

R.H.

GRAY
SQUIRREL

2"

R.F.

R.H.

WOODCHUCK

R.F.

R.H.

R.H.

R.F.

MUSKRAT

R.H.

FOX
SQUIRREL

6"

L.F.

R.H.

R.F.

R.H.

BEAVER

PORCUPINE

Larger Rodents